2-1-04

To Viveca
With Love

Ja Carrol

What people are saying about Dr. Carolle

"Dr. Carolle's new book about balancing your life is for anyone of any age, but especially for women - and for the men who love them."
Louise Lauture, *NY*

•

"... **Dr. Carolle** makes you want to get better-She's what makes anyone a fighter."
Ozzie Roberts, *San Diego Union-Tribune*

•

"... Her endeavors should be carried out far and wide across the country."
Joyce F. Nau, *North County Loan Services*

•

"... She can especially relate to women in transition who are trying to figure out who the hell they are."
Deborah Farmer, *Patient of Dr. Carolle's*

•

"... **Dr. Carolle** is charming, provocative and fun."
Susan Flansburg, *The Leader*

•

"Once again ...stupendous! Such a natural motivator!!..."
Kim Edstrom, *Medical Media, Inc.*

•

"... Nothing less than charismatic."
Participant in a Dr. Carolle seminar

•

"I couldn't believe you emailed me so quickly in response to my embarrassing question."
Visitor to Dr. Carolle's website

•

"It was unanimous!! You were a great hit - to a real mixed bag of ladies."
Victoria L. Spilkin, *American Association of University Women*

•

"... **Dr. Carolle** explains life-altering things in a way that make them more palatable to hear and face about ourselves."
Judith Jeannotte, Social Worker

•

"I can't sing your praise enough. You are the epitome of what a doctor should be. I never knew what it was like to have such faith and trust in a doctor."
In a letter from Debbie Gregorovic

•

"Mind, Body, Soul and Money" is easy to read, interesting, informative and compelling."
Laurie Gill, *Jewelry Designer*

MIND,
BODY,
SOUL &
MONEY

MIND, BODY, SOUL & MONEY

Putting Your Life In Balance

CAROLLE JEAN-MURAT, M.D.

MOSLEY
PUBLISHING
GROUP

www.mosleypublishing.com

Mosley Publishing Group
San Diego, California
www.mosleypublishing.com

Editing by Karen Louise Wilkening, Expert Editing, Ink.

ISBN 1-886185-13-1
1st printing, August, 2002

Printed in the United States of America
Precision Litho

Disclaimer

The author of this book does not dispense medical advice or prescribe the use of any technique as a form of treatment for physical or medical problems without the advice of a physician, either directly or indirectly. The intent of the author is only to offer information of a general nature to help you in your quest for emotional, physical, and spiritual well-being. In the event you use any of the information in this book for yourself, which is your constitutional right, the author and the publisher assume no responsibility for your actions.

*This book is dedicated to my alter ego, Charles Rene, M.D.,
for his dedication and for his inspiration. To Professeur Aubies Franck,
Professeur Arthur Laroche, Professeur Leon Franck, Soeur Josepha, FDM,
and to the memory of Philippe Jules of La Vallee de Jacmel, Haiti.
To the founders of CODEVA (Coude-a-Coude Pour le Development
Valleen), visionaries who dared to come out of the box and make a difference.
To Louise and Joseph Lauture and those members of the Vallean Fraternity
who tirelessly work for the betterment of mankind,
To Chantal and Serge Rene, and to Michael Zephir for his excellent work
with the children of La Vallee de Jacmel.*

*To my father Joseph Karl Jean (Tete Chauve), my sisters Marise,
Elsie and Massou, my brother Lesly and his wife Louanna,
and my brothers Jacky and Harry.*

*To the memory of my mother Marie Anne Lamercie Murat (Silotte), to Julia
Jean (Tatante), Richard (Dick) Philpott, M.D., and Wilfrid Jr. Jean-Pierre, all of
whom passed away during the time when I was searching for myself.*

To the people of the world without a voice.

Contents

Acknowledgments

*There are many wonderful people to thank
for their support and assistance.*

My dear husband *Albert*, who supports me in every decision I make…
Meggan Lennon of Peppercom Communications, *Deborah Sandgren*, *Andy
Hilton, Michele Tinkler, Tom Topinka, Jennifer Haig, Dr. Fred Waddel, Erin
Loughney, Randi Oster, Gwen Reichbach, Ph.D., Jay Kearns, Kathleen Gurney,
Ph.D., Richard Sherman* (Mr. Modem) at GE Center for Financial Learning, and
Raymond Loewe of College Money, who all helped conceive the idea of writing
this "four-legged" book…
and *Deborah Mosley* of Mosley Publishing, my patient publisher.

I will be forever grateful to *Aliya Khan, MD…Minh & Myelin Ho, MD* and
staff whose office space I shared…*Charlotte Quiroga* and the staff
of the Sycuan Medical and Dental Clinic, who provided an oasis for my patients
and for me.

Special recognition goes to *Linda* and *Clifford La Chappa* of the
Barona Band of Kumeyaay Nation…*Danny Tucker* and his sister *Charlotte* of the
Sycuan Band of Kumeyaay Nation…*Patricia A. Roberts…Joselande Jean-
Gilles…John Blackwood* of Community Donor Services…*Kathleen Moore* of
Kathleen Communications, Inc…*Sheri* and *Robert Thurman… Reginald G.
Hailey and Thekima Mayasa Hailey…*the wise and wonderful *Louise L.
Hay…*my fellow Rotarians at the Southeast San Diego Rotary…my patients,

my family, friends, colleagues, and all the other caring people who helped to make the Haiti project a reality while I was searching for myself.

To *Denise Giusti-Bradford*, my friend and therapist...*Robert Leak*, Holistic Health Practitioner...*Laurie Gill*, my walking partner and sounding board...and my friend *Edna Parish*, whose great cooking kept me going.

I would also like to thank the following people for their unwavering support given in so many ways: *James Schaeffer, MD* and his wife *Ghislaine*...*Iyabo Daramola, MD*...*Louise O'Shaughnessy, MD*...*Trisha Weir*...*Gloria Brockman*...*Luckie Judson*...*Charlotte Jackson*...*June Blacknell*...*Mary Bush*...*Margaret Peacock*...
Hallie Stubbs...and *Carlene Lamb*.

Many thanks also to *Derek Dingle* of Black Enterprise Magazine, and his assistant *Hyacinth B. Carbon*...*Donald B. Throne* of the Center for Fiduciary Studies...*Robert L. Wallace*, President and Founder of The Bith Group, Inc...*Ginita Wall, CPA, CFP,* Director of the Women's Institute for Financial Education (WIFE.org)...*Bernard Surovsky*, Financial Consultant...and *Pamela J. Givens,* Financial Consultant and Retirement Plan Specialist (ssbfcs.com/ givens) for their suggestions and help with the Money section of this book.

To my neighbors *Margaret and Vincent O'Hara, Shirley Trimodero, Linda and Michael Rice*, and *Lois Shade* for giving me plants for my personal "mental health garden"...and to *Eduardo* for helping me transform my yard into that beautiful garden.

And how could I write a book without my loyal team?
Special thanks go to *Sirocoro Doumbia*, my computer guru...
Leslie K. Joyce, MPH, the "Queen of Franglish," who patiently "translates" my notes and first drafts into more recognizable English...and to *Karen Wilkening*, owner of Expert Editing, Ink, my keen editor – who brainstorms with me from start to finish, refines the material,
and polishes it to a shine.

Preface

I was born in Port-au-Prince, the capital of Haiti, in 1950, the first-born daughter of Joseph Karl Jean, and Marie Anne Lamercie Murat. My mother's father was Mirabeau Murat, a renowned Voodoo priest and indigenous healer from Bizoton, a small town outside of Port-au-Prince. None of my family on my mother's side had ever graduated from primary school. In contrast, my father was from a family of lawyers, judges, and teachers. My paternal grandfather was a pharmacist, but also an alcoholic.

There are no social programs to help impoverished women in Haiti. When I was 4, my mother was separated from my father and was expecting twins. She could no longer afford to care for all of her children, so my sister, Marise, and I went to live with my paternal grandmother Eugenie. We called her Grandma. She lived with her daughter, Julia who never married. We called her Tatante. The occasional visits to see my mother were so upsetting that I promised her that I would become important and take care of her so she would never have to cry again. It was then that I made the decision to never allow myself to be stuck in the same educational, economical, and socially dependent position as my mother.

When I was 9 years old, I became very ill, and my grandfather Mirabeau, the Voodoo priest, restored my health through his healing powers. This made such a great impression on me that *I decided I would become a healer*.

Grandma was a healer in her own right. When she was 32 years old, she told her abusive husband, Emmanuel, to leave. She never divorced him because she was Catholic. She remained single, and worked hard to educate my father and Tatante.

Grandma had a special bag, full of many smaller bags, each one filled with a different herb. She knew all the herbs by name, and just how much to give you to make you feel better. Her "primary care" doctor was a folk healer, but she lived far away from us. Grandma visited her doctor every six months, spending the whole day receiving massages with special oils and drinking healing potions. Medical doctors were expensive and were consulted only if she was really sick. Her approach worked, as she outlived all of her medical doctors and died at home peacefully at age 87.

At age 16, I spent part of the summer in a small town in the northern part of Haiti. Next door to our residence was a small clinic. Joseph was a male nurse who worked at the clinic one day a week. I asked if I could help him. People came to the clinic from all over, and were waiting at the door before the clinic opened. This clinic received donations of medications and supplies from a religious group in the United States. Joseph listened to each person's complaint with great patience. In payment for his services, Joseph would receive live chickens, bags of fruit, eggs, sometimes a little change.

I learned at the clinic that these people believed in injections – the more painful they were, the better they would work! When I noticed that some patients received injections of sterile water, I questioned Joseph. He said that since there was not enough medication to go around, his only alternative was to give harmless injections of sterile water. Most of these trusting people were cured because they believed that Joseph had administered medication to heal them! I was beginning to realize that a large part of the healing process was based on the belief that *the healer would help the patient.*

Grandma was a very strong woman, and she had very strong friends. It was difficult for a woman to live alone, "without a man to protect her." She refused to live with a man who was not her husband. One of her friends, Edith, suffered from tuberculosis. Before taking her dying breath, she asked Grandma to prop her up with a pillow because she did not want to face death lying down.

Grandma taught me never to be afraid. I can still hear her voice.

"When you are in a strange place, especially in the wee hours of the night, you cannot show that you are afraid. You cannot walk, looking about, showing fear that someone is going to kidnap you. Your steps have to say: 'here I come, let me go by.' Keep your head high on your shoulders, prop up your bosom, and look straight ahead. When each foot hits the ground, it has to be with firmness and confidence; take long strides. And, if you are walking in the middle of the night and you come across the devil, or the loup-garou, you cannot show you are afraid. You just have to pray, 'This is the cross of Jesus, stay away from the cross of Jesus.' Otherwise, be ready to spit in the devil's face."

I grew up looking forward to growing old and being like Grandma – wise, loved, respected, and *in control*. I promised myself I would be different from the other girls who dreamed of being married, having children, and being subordinate to their men. I would be smart and go as far as any man.

I was 11 years old when I realized that my mother was also a healer. During one of my few visits to see my mother, someone knocked on the door to ask for her help in delivering one of the neighbor's babies. I begged my mother to let me go with her. I promised not to bother her. My heart raced as I led us through the night with a small lamp. It was an exhilarating experience. I decided that I would not mind helping to bring babies into this world, but would have to learn to deal with all of the blood.

When I left Haiti in 1970, bound for the United States, I was 20 years old and had big dreams. I hoped to be accepted into medical school at a French-speaking university in Europe. I dreamed of returning to Haiti as a doctor, and being able to help the poor people. Grandma always talked about Albert Schweitzer's hospital, where the poor received free medical care. Maybe someday I could build a hospital just like it in Haiti.

I was supposed to stay in Brooklyn for only a few months when I arrived in the US, but ended up staying two years. I did not have the opportunity to go to Europe. I became reacquainted with an old friend, Nicole. She was as determined to become a doctor as I was. She knew Nadine, a former classmate from Haiti who was a first year student at the Autonomous University of Guadalajara Medical School, in Mexico. Nadine told us that if we were accepted at her school, and had enough money to pay for the first year, we could apply for student loans in the US to cover the other three years. I was lucky that my father and stepmother Eka were supportive, and that I was able to work odd jobs and save money.

Nicole and I were accepted at the medical school in Mexico. We started on August 4, 1972. At the time, I spoke Haitian and French. I needed to learn Spanish. Since my goal was to be accepted into a postgraduate program in the United States, I would also have to learn English. Piece of cake!

During our last year of medical school, we were lucky to have the help of some Jewish-American students. We made special arrangements for clerkships during the last semester of medical school at the Kingsbrook Jewish Medical Center, located in Brooklyn and associated with Down State University Medical School.

To be accepted into a post-graduate program in the US as we had planned, we needed to spend a year interning in an accredited hospital, and another year of Servicio Social (social services) with the Department of Public Health in Mexico. At the end of that year, I took the final exam and obtained my Physician and Surgeons diploma, the Titulo de Medico Cirujano. Meanwhile, I still had to pass the exam given by the Educational Council for Foreign Medical Graduates.

We heard that internships were available through the Ministry of Health at the University of the West Indies, in Jamaica. This hospital was known for handling rare diseases, most of which we had only read about in books. We were told that the training was good, and that medical students from England and Canada chose clerkships in Jamaica during the winter months. Several of us opted to do this, as we believed that we could acquire sufficient experience to pass the foreign medical graduate exam. The pay was good, and the food, people, and reggae music were icing on the cake.

I was lucky to be trained by nurse midwives in Jamaica, who taught me that birthing was a natural event. I learned that given sufficient time, any woman could deliver without need for an episiotomy. The rate of Cesarean section was only 4%, compared to at least 20% in the US.

I returned to rural Mexico and spent a year in community medicine, delivering babies, often without running water or electricity. I was accepted for postgraduate training in obstetrics and gynecology at Mount Sinai Medical Center, in Milwaukee, Wisconsin, where I nearly froze to death! I finally visited San Diego during the winter months. When I realized that I could stick my hand outside the car window and let the breeze flow through my fingers without freezing, I knew that San Diego would be my home. I did not care that San Diego had few black doctors, and no other black female ob-gyn. I've never minded breaking the ice. For four years, I remained the only female ob-gyn in the hospital where I practiced, and the only black female ob-gyn in private practice for 12 years.

The last two months of my training were spent at UCLA. By then, I was licensed to practice medicine in Wisconsin, and had earned reciprocity to practice in California. I had also passed the written board for my specialty. Two years later, after passing my oral board examination, I became a board-certified obstetrician and gynecologist, and eventually a "Fellow of the American College of Obstetricians and Gynecologists."

When I think about it, few doctors have had my diverse experience when it comes to healing. I was seriously ill and cured by my grandfather, a traditional healer with primitive diagnostic methods. I personally know many people from a variety of backgrounds who view illness and death as due to natural or supernatural forces. These people do not believe in the healing power of pills, but believe leaves and other natural objects have mystical power. Others associate the healing process with touch and prayer.

It was easy for me to apply all I had learned in my private, solo practice. Soon, I was known as the doctor who had a holistic approach to caring for patients, who believed that patients have the right to accept or refuse care. I was willing to work with patients who elected alternative medicine techniques. I refused to have a busy practice that did not allow me the time to really listen to my patients. I felt obligated to tell my patients what the medical books recommended, but at the same time, I was supportive of alternative care and healing practices.

But through the years, it became more and more difficult to practice medicine in the manner I desired. As I see it, practicing medicine is often like using a sixth sense, where clinical knowledge *plus* what is happening to the individual patient guides my decisions. However, our medical system is not always set up to support what is best for the patient.

One night, I was called to see a patient who was in labor and experiencing fetal distress. I performed a Caesarean section. On the way home, I realized that while my clinical judgment was correct, it was somewhat biased due to the fear of litigation. I had not followed my instinct to wait awhile before delivering the baby. When I got home, I threw up. I decided to quit obstetrics, regardless of the financial repercussions.

A minor incident in 1995 changed my life drastically. I lost my temper in public and created a scene. That night, I lay awake, unable to fall asleep. I realized that the incident was a symptom that I had lost control of my life, I had hit bottom. Today, when I speak of this incident, I refer to it as my mid-life crisis. It happened when I was 45 years old, had been in private practice for 13 years, and was becoming disillusioned.

At that time, San Diego and Minneapolis/St. Paul were the US centers for managed care. In less than 10 years, I watched as the proportion of patients covered by managed care health plans went from 20% to 80%. It no longer mattered how good a physician I was. The fact was, if I did not belong to an HMO, I could no longer care for my patients who did belong. According to managed care, specialists were no longer necessary. Now patients could be seen by physician's assistants and nurse practitioners for routine gynecological care. If a problem arose, the patient's family physician, the HMO gatekeeper, would refer the patient to a gynecologist, if necessary.

I was told that my only chance of survival in San Diego was to become certified as a primary care provider. I began the primary care training with a lot of resentment. Four months later, while studying the psychiatry module, I realized that I had all of the symptoms of depression. Being the good girl that I was, I pushed through and received my diploma.

As a little girl, I had decided that I would be in charge of my life. I set goals for myself, committed myself to them, and worked hard to achieve them. Receiving my certification for primary care made me feel like a traitor. Hundreds of thousands of women throughout the world were dying due to the lack of an experienced healer like me. I did not have to remain in San Diego, or the US, for that matter. Although the political turmoil in Haiti prevented me from returning, I could go anywhere in the world. I was fluent in five languages, and could learn another if need be. Why betray myself?

Aside from career challenges, my personal life was in upheaval as well. Following the death of Grandma in 1991, I lost five close friends in a short period of time. I was becoming painfully aware of my own mortality. I no longer felt I had a long life ahead of me. At the same time, I was ending a five-year relationship. I did a lot of soul searching, but I failed to listen to my inner wisdom about my career and continued my private practice.

In 1987, I created a nonprofit organization and produced a series of 30-minute health videos, which were later broadcast by the local cable television station. I decided to devote my time to writing and becoming a motivational speaker. I spoke of my life experiences, and tried to teach women that "the sky was the limit." I continued as an assistant clinical professor at UCSD School of Medicine and mentored minority students through San Diego State University.

As time passed, the situation in my practice worsened. Due to rising malpractice costs, in 1999 I chose to stop performing surgeries. Four days after making this decision, I decided that it was time for me to return to Haiti to use my skills. I planned to join Dr. Charles Rene's team of healthcare providers and educators on their next trip to Haiti. Dr. Rene, also of Haitian descent, owns a private practice in New Orleans, but twice a year since 1984, he has traveled with his team to La Vallee de Jacmel, a beautiful town nestled in the southeastern mountains of Haiti, overlooking the Caribbean Sea. The People of La Vallee built a small hospital, in 1980, by asking each villager to bring a rock and a bucket of sand. Later, they built a Lycee to educate the poor children, most of them walking for hours, on empty stomachs, to reach the school.

My whole family, including my husband, Albert, also Haitian, had looked forward to the day when I would return to Haiti as a missionary. My mother lived in Miami, a short distance from my sisters, Marise and Elsie. She had been traveling to and from Haiti, providing help to poor families. Once, she dreamed that I would be able to return to Haiti, we would build a school next to the hospital, and provide warm meals to the children every day. "Children cannot learn on empty stomachs," she would say adamantly. "I will personally buy cornmeal and beans and cook them myself." Unfortunately, a few days after finalizing the details with Dr. Rene, my mother suffered a stroke, which resulted in memory disturbances and personality changes. When I told her that I was finally going to Haiti, she replied, "Haiti, I do not like Haiti anymore. I don't ever want to go back there," she said. I cried inconsolably.

My mother's health slowly deteriorated. I was so angry. How dare she die without seeing me return to Haiti? She suffered several more strokes, eventually becoming paralyzed and bedridden. She was in and out of the hospital. She told us to let her go, that she did not want to suffer any longer.

Soon, she could not talk or swallow. We decided that she should return to the home she shared with her sister, Audencie, to die in peace with hospice care.

But it is impossible to predict the exact time of death. Should I cancel my trip to Haiti so I could be there when she died, and attend the funeral? Would there always be an excuse for me not to go to Haiti? I was my mother's oldest daughter and I was supposed to attend her funeral. I was guilt-ridden even before the fact.

My mother passed away before my scheduled trip, but more family tragedy struck close to my departure to Haiti, again tearing me apart about staying or going. It was very hard for me to leave, but I had to go. The trip to Haiti was difficult for me, seeing the abject poverty in which most people there lived, including some of my own family.

Back at my office, the situation grew worse. I learned that the insurance companies had never been billed for most of my work, including my last surgery. Patients were not billed for their portion for almost two years. I was very upset. I would awaken in the middle of the night with my heart racing. I contemplated quitting my practicing altogether, but felt an obligation to my patients. I became very resentful that I had to provide care and then had to fight to be reimbursed. It was a very stressful time in my life. I felt out of control and hated the feeling.

My niece, Judive, graduated from Ohio University's medical school on June 2, 2000. She had always wanted to be a doctor like her "Tattie" Carolle. When I walked with her to the podium to receive her diploma, it was the proudest moment of my life. To return home, I had a stopover in Dallas. There was a storm in Dallas so we were stuck on the ground, inside the plane, for awhile. The pilot told us that no one was available to open the outside door because so many planes were landing at the same time. I began to experience fear; I was stuck inside and needed to get out. I could see workers placing luggage in carts through the small window of the plane. The longer we were stuck, the more I panicked. I tried to breathe slowly because it felt like I was suffocating. They finally opened the door, but it had seemed an eternity. I worried about the next leg of my journey back to San Diego, but nothing happened until I took another airplane trip.

This time I was on a book tour in New York, promoting my book, *Natural Pregnancy A-Z*. I was visiting my mother's sister, Alourdes, who lived in Spring Valley, when the phone rang. It was Haiti. One of my female cousins had died of a stroke at age 48. Tante Alourdes, still grieving from her sister's death, passed out on the floor. The doorbell rang. My half-brother, Harry, was there to take me to my long-time friend Nicole's house in Jamaica Heights. I did not even have a chance to say goodbye to my aunt.

I stayed with Nicole and her family for two days. She was worried about me; she had never seen me so pessimistic. She could see I was over-whelmed by the stress in my life. And New York City, with its high-speed lifestyle, is not the place for someone under a lot of stress. I attended four book signings and a seminar in those two days. My brother, Lesly, and his wife, Louanna, and their three children, came for one book signing at Barnes and Noble Bookstore. That night at Lesly's house, I could not sleep. It seemed to me as if the whole world was caving in. The next morning, I was needed to retrieve an important e-mail. The computer was in the basement, but I could not manage the few steps that lead down to it. If I went down there, I thought I would be buried alive. Anxiety had gotten the best of me and I knew it.

Thus began my journey to find my balance. It was not easy. I had to let go of a lot of baggage, change my overall outlook on life, and cut a few umbilical cords. I had to gain perspective in order to make wiser choices. It had to be done, so I did it. *Now I want to help you do the same.*

If you follow at least some of the advice in this book, you may be saved from having to go through what I did. Since that time, I have learned that there is a lot involved in being healthy – more than taking care of your body – and also more than nurturing your mind and spirit. I discovered first-hand that the financial aspects of your life have a great impact on your overall health too.

I began to see the common thread connecting many women's reported health problems – financial stress. Many women traveled from afar to see me because their own healthcare providers could not help them. In actuality, these women did not need more estrogen or testosterone, or herbs or sleeping pills to sleep, they needed to take charge of their financial lives. This problem can affect women from all walks of life, and at any age.

After returning from New York, I reduced my private practice by seeing patients on a cash basis only, to get away from the insurance company horrors. I was fortunate to have the financial capacity to do so. Mind you, I was not rich. Most doctors do not make as much money as some people think.

I had learned to save for possible emergency situations just like this. It freed me to heal and to work on the other important aspects of my health.

I learned so much about what works and what doesn't that I couldn't keep it to myself. I love to empower people, especially women. So I decided to write this book to help you find your way to becoming healthy and balanced. Mind, body, soul, money – Like a four-legged table, if just one leg is off kilter, the table will wobble or even fall over. We're going to prevent that.

Introduction

At every stage of life – from birth to death – it is vitally important to have a balanced life for health and happiness. Most of us, including me, were not born into such an atmosphere and had no model for it. The most difficult challenge for all of us is creating and maintaining balance in our personal lives, in the midst of an ever-changing world. A healthy balanced life is not easy to achieve, but I know that it's possible because I work on it every day for myself, and for my patients.

I am a gynecologist, not a psychologist, priestess, or financial planner – but I've written this book to include the components of *mind, soul* and *finances* because my approach to health differs from that of the average American physician. My background in Haiti and my life experiences give me a *holistic perspective* on health that takes into account the physical, plus the mental, spiritual and financial realms. As a holistic healer, I believe that all of these components should be attended to individually, but also acknowledged as inextricably intertwined. All four aspects must be kept equally in balance for a healthy life.

This book is unique because it contains very personal anecdotes about my life, interesting stories about my friends, family members, mentors, and patients, and because it gives you Dr. Carolle's preventive "prescriptions" for health in all areas of your life.

Imparting balanced holistic health is the work I've chosen as a doctor. It is also the reason I've written this book for you.

Section One: Mind – *Your Mental Health*
Good mental health is the cornerstone to a balanced life. Life is full of ups and downs, and stress is inevitable. There are secrets to learning how to cope with stress and maintain a positive attitude toward life. Especially among women, mental health is directly related to our relationships with our intimate partners, children, relatives, friends, career, and community. Women typically care for everyone else before taking care of themselves. I will show you how to learn to value yourself as much as you value the lives of others, and carve out time for your own well being.

Section Two: Body – *Your Physical Health*
How you take care of your body determines the quality of your life. Many illnesses are related to lifestyle choices. This section provides you with what you need to know to be physically healthy in today's world. Preventive care is the key not easily obtained from most doctors. Learn how disease prevention can be cheap and easy.

Section Three: Soul – *Your Spiritual Health*
You will discover the part your spiritual health plays in your overall well being. If you are happy with your present spiritual life, that is wonderful. You can spend more time on the other sections of the book. But, if you are like many women, including myself, who abandoned organized religion as you grew older, this section may help point you toward personal enlightenment.

Section Four: Money – *Your Financial Health*
Many physical complaints can be traced to the financial stressors in your life. If you are not in control of your finances, you may feel as though you are no longer in control of your life. I will guide you through the process of documenting your present financial situation, setting long-term financial goals, learning ways to get out of debt, and saving for your future. *You do not have to be rich in order to be financially secure.*

Women often pay little attention to their finances and, as a result, our children fail to learn what they need to know about financial planning. I have included a section about how to educate yourself and your children about finances.

Another area covered is healthcare insurance and how it affects us. I'll shed some light on HMOs, PPOs, IPAs, the entire alphabet soup and terminology of the healthcare system.

Section One

MIND

Your
Mental
Health

Your Mental Health

I chose to put the "mind" section first in this book for a reason. In my opinion, although all the components are important for a balanced life, *good mental health is the cornerstone.* Your mind serves as the captain of your ship. Each of the other components, body, soul and finances, rely on the stewardship, competence, and managerial abilities of your mind.

We typically use our mental abilities to meet the demands of our lives – to plan and keep schedules, and to navigate daily or weekly events. But the mind is capable of so much more. It can be tapped to assist us in every other aspect of our lives.

Developing good mental health requires the use of a number of keys, each of them having to do with *relationships*–your relationship with yourself, and your relationships with other people, whether they are family, playmates, companions, teammates, co-workers, bosses, employees, landlords, students, or complete strangers. *There is value in every relationship* because you can use it for self-enlightenment and growth.

RELATIONSHIP WITH YOURSELF

Having a healthy relationship with yourself begins with *knowing yourself*. **Who are you?** What are your dreams, goals, and values? What do you want out of life? What makes you happy and fulfilled? What are your feelings at any given time? Why do you do the things you do? What do you believe in? What drives you? What are you passionate about?

Do you do things out of a sense of obligation to others, because of expectations others have placed on you, or because you *want* to do them? Is your sense of self-esteem based on feedback, both supportive and critical, from people around you, or is it grounded in a clear sense of who you are, your convictions, and your sense of self-worth? The wise Greek saying "Know Thyself" can also be translated as "Know Your Enemy" because most people are their own worst enemy!

> *I am responsible for what I see.*
> *I choose the feelings I experience.*
> *I decide upon the goal I would achieve.*
> *Everything that seems to happen to me I ask for,*
> *and receive as I have asked.*
> —A Course in Miracles

In today's world, emphasis is placed on youth, and peri-menopause and menopause can be periods of anxiety and emotional devastation. After age 50, the average age of menopause, the signs of aging become more apparent. This is also the time when other important changes come to the forefront. Women who have never worked outside of the home may feel that their lives have little meaning because their children are no longer at home. Some women find themselves divorced, with few skills necessary for re-entering the working force. Women who built their lives around their children may opt to go to school or seek employment now that their children have left home. On the other hand, women who have had a busy professional life may be asking themselves, "What's life *really* about?" Other women who delayed motherhood may still have young children at home. Some women may find themselves attempting to cope with the challenges of the "sandwich generation," having to care for aging parents and growing children at the same time. With all of these challenges, a woman's self-esteem may be at a low point.

Coping mechanisms can be stretched to the limit, especially if hormonal changes are occurring in tandem.

Self-esteem

Self-esteem is a thinking game. How we think about ourselves is how we are going to relate to others, and influences how we work, play, and learn. Self-esteem includes our assessment of ourselves, our worthiness, the extent to which we see ourselves able to succeed, and able to overcome challenges. If our self-esteem is low, we do not see ourselves as successful, we isolate ourselves and tend to feel defenseless and unloved. On the other hand, if our self-esteem is high, we are poised and confident and less likely to be influenced by others. People who triumph in life tend to have a tremendous sense of self-esteem.

If we have high self-esteem, we treat ourselves well and are treated well by others. This, in turn, reinforces our belief in ourselves and, when combined with our past experiences, enables us to believe that our future endeavors will be successful. When a specific goal is not accomplished as planned, an individual with high self-esteem may choose instead to view it as a stepping-stone to something better, greater and more enriching. And they go on.

Many people spend entire lifetimes deferring dreams and postponing the enjoyment of each moment, all the while thinking that tomorrow will be more fulfilling and less stressful. Regardless of age, occupation, handicap, heritage, or environment, individuals have the ability, and the responsibility, to control their own destinies and the choice to create balance in their lives.

If you have high self-esteem, you will:

- Not be afraid to stand out in a crowd.
- Not compromise your high standards, which includes not taking recreational drugs, and not smoking, drinking too much or otherwise living dangerously.

> *When I was 10 years old, I had the first opportunity to witness my mother, a midwife, deliver a baby. Later, I was trained*

by nurse midwives in Jamaica, where the rate of Caesarean sections was low compared to America. My patients were told that I would be called for an emergency C-section in the event of fetal distress. Upon arriving in the operating room, with the woman already anesthetized and prepped for surgery, I would reassess the woman's condition. Sometimes I observed that the woman's condition had improved, and then reconsidered whether a C-section was necessary. Fear would creep in and my confidence in my ability to make the right decision faltered. I envisioned myself standing in a courtroom defending my decisions. It is true that a C-section is often more convenient and, at that time, insurance companies reimbursed more for them. One day, I performed a C-section, knowing that I had given in to my fear of being sued. I went home, threw up, and quit a very lucrative aspect of my doctoring so that I would never compromise on this issue again.

- Not give in to a system you don't respect.

Due to the smaller and smaller reimbursements from insurance companies, I found myself having to see more and more patients in order to meet my overhead expenses. So, I decided to accept patients solely on a cash pay basis. I made this decision to protect me and my patients from the limitations of the managed care system. It was difficult, but I decided that I would be happier doing business my own way.

- Not be afraid to speak out against injustice.
- Dare to have big dreams, commit to them, and make them happen, even if you have never met anyone who has succeeded.

I knew since I was a young girl that I could do anything I wanted. I chose to be a healer – a doctor. It was a long, arduous road with many obstacles besides being a woman. I had to learn Spanish to go to medical school, then English to do my post-graduate training. I lived and trained in warm and cold countries, and learned about many different cultures. Fourteen years after I graduated from high school I realized my big dream and became a doctor.

Attitude is Everything

The real key to staying mentally healthy is to maintain positive feelings about yourself. Eleanor Roosevelt said, *"No one can make you feel inferior without your consent."* Successful people usually have tremendous self-confidence–they look at life as a creative adventure. This can be accomplished by being true to yourself and your goals, staying focused on your personal values, and linking your goals together to maintain a healthy outlook on life, regardless of the expectations of others. Being mentally healthy means being in control of your own destiny.

A positive attitude can be a potent weapon against serious illness. In a study of men who had heart attacks, 21 out of 25 men who were pessimists died from the heart attack compared to only 6 out of 25 men who were optimistic.

My family was poor, and the country I grew up in was ruled by a dictatorship. There was so much pain around me that I decided at a young age that I would not suffer any longer; I decided to look for the positive in everything. I have been called a pathologic optimist, but I don't mind. I have been asked many times if I encountered racial prejudice. My answer is no, I did not see it. I attribute this to the fact that I see the good in everyone, and always trust people until they show they are not worthy of that trust. I am ready to learn from everyone. Also, I treat everyone the same regardless of who they are or where they came from. In return, I am received with open arms.

Self-Acceptance as We Age

Many of us seek to find something wrong with who we are. Many of us do not like what we see in the mirror; we want to be taller, shorter, thinner, or fatter. We want to have darker skin and baste in the sun to get a "healthy tan," subsequently increasing our risk of skin cancer. If we have straight hair, we curl it; if it is curly, we want it straight, and on and on.

Americans live in a youth-oriented society that bombards us daily with images of youthful superiority. In many other societies, old age brings respect, perquisites, and honor. Elders have more prestige and power than do the young, and their advice is eagerly sought. Millions of dollars are spent in this country in the attempt to ward off aging, and many people opt for cosmetic surgeries to stay young looking. Some women take natural hormone products, such as human growth hormone, to replace what their bodies no longer produce, but there is no research to show that this works. Long-term, scientific studies are needed to discern whether these treatments are worth the excessive costs. Human growth hormone treatment costs about $20,000 per year.

Aging is often associated with failing health and lessening prowess. We need to learn to accept ourselves the way we are, and to know that it is okay to grow old. Many of us do not want to age naturally, we want to have buff, wrinkle-free bodies, and therefore, continue to support the multi-billion dollar industry of plastic surgery and cosmetics.

Modern medicine allows us to live longer and lead a more independent life. To a great degree, the advances of modern medicine do, in fact, permit the elderly to live longer. The proportion of the population over age 65 is mushrooming as the baby-boomers age. Genetically, we are predisposed to die and age. Despite our efforts and the efforts of modern medicine, the human genetic clock has its limits. Currently the maximum life span is 115 years, and only a very few make it. Until we gain the ability to alter genes safely, the attempt to recapture youth will remain an elusive search. What we need are blueprints to teach us how to accept aging gracefully.

The key is allowing our mind to accept the changes that occur in our bodies, while enjoying life to the fullest. Perhaps we need to make lists of important things to remember, and take up yoga or stretch a little more to maintain our agility, flexibility and fitness. If we use these tools, the need for plastic surgery, anti-aging creams, liposuction, and hair dye will lessen.

I grew up hating my black kinky hair, only to learn that some people could not stand their "too straight" hair. I was one of the three tallest girls in my Haitian town. Not only was I very tall, I was also very skinny. My little brother, Lesly, used to call me Gran' Pele, a witch character from our stories who dressed in black and flew on a broomstick. While studying in Mexico, I attended a fair in one of the southern states where people tended to be shorter. I remember visiting an exotic animal barn, but most people seemed to be looking at me instead of the animals. I was always too tall, too skinny, the only black, the only woman, the only one with an accent, most of my life. Sometimes I wished that I could be a man, or a less-assertive woman, or a white woman, but not because I was uncomfortable being black – I had never had to deal with racism growing up in Haiti – but because I still hated my hair. I was not only straightening it, I was dyeing the gray roots every two weeks!

In my heritage, one never worried about getting older; I grew up looking forward to growing old and being like Grandma–beautiful, wise, loved and respected. The opposite is true in American culture, where aging is associated with mental and physical deterioration. I have had many patients who dread the idea of growing old. No one believed me when I said that I looked forward to menopause!

At age 48, I cut my hair very short because I became tired of forever straightening it. Since then, I even made peace with my graying roots. I made up my mind to feel free of "correcting" my age.

Learn to Say NO

"I must govern the clock, not be governed by it!"
—Golda Meir

Your time and energy are precious commodities and are not to be wasted. Learn to value *your time* as much as you value others'. There is a tendency for women to put themselves last on their priority list.

Learn to say NO if you are asked to do something that "doesn't feel right." This is part of honoring yourself. At first it can be difficult, but with practice, it becomes easier and easier.

Listen to Your Body

Your body will let your mind know when you are under stress. You need to listen and be aware of what it is trying to tell you. A lot of people self-medicate. If we have a headache, we take a pill; when we are tired, we take energy boosters. If we take the time to find the cause, it will save us a lot of discomfort, as well as a lot of money.

Over the years I have cared for many women with symptoms such as irregular bleeding, headaches, and hot flashes. Often, if they had been taking medication, they wanted a stronger dose because they thought it was no longer working. After questioning them, I would often learn that their life situation was the cause of their problems. They had to learn to find their own solutions, and not look for a solution in a pill.

Listen to Your Intuition

Intuition is a way of "knowing before you know." Learning to listen to our intuition can be a great self-protection tool. Letting your mind listen to your internal warning systems can save a lot of grief. According to Gavin de Becker, author of the bestseller *The Gift of Fear: Survival Signals That Protect Us from Violence*, our instincts alert us to danger, which may keep us from stepping into dangerous situations.

We do not want to be overcautious or paranoid, but we should pay attention when we hear warning bells going off in our heads. How many times have you ignored your intuition? Were you ever ripped off by a "deal" even though you were forewarned by your intuition that it sounded too good to be true? What message is your mind giving your body?

> *A few years ago, I waited in a long line in a post office in Brooklyn, New York to cash a postal money order. The cashier took a quick look at my driver's license, shoved it back to me under the small opening of the cashier's window and barked, "Your driver's license is not valid." Indeed, my driver's license had expired, but she had not taken the time to look at the pink card, which stated that it had been extended for another four years.*

Having the cashier return all my paperwork made something snap. All of a sudden, I split into two different people: One, a mischievous little girl floating up by the ceiling looking down at myself at the cashier's window in front of a packed room. The other was screaming, yelling, jumping up and down, and telling a panic-stricken crowd everything that had happened over the past two years. I clearly remember the fear in everyone's eyes. It wasn't until much later that I found out about the term "going postal."

At that point in time my life was in upheaval. My Grandma, my best friend and confidant, died in her sleep at age 87. I lost five close friends in a short period of time. I ended a five-year relationship. I was becoming painfully aware of my own mortality. For the first time, I no longer felt I had a long life ahead of me. I made the difficult decision to quit obstetrics after a ten year practice. Managed care was getting its grip on San Diego, and I could not practice medicine the way I felt was good for my patients.

I made some changes, but retrospectively I see now that I did not do enough. I eventually closed my private practice, dismissed my staff, and decided to join Dr. Mylien Ho, my gynecologist, and share her staff, while keeping my own medical billing services.

I got another wake up call when I got a message that my friend Deborah was at a rehab center due to a large cancerous bone marrow tumor. After the surgery she had to learn to walk again. Seeing Deborah in that hospital bed made me realize that it was time that I started to take care of myself. I called Denise, my therapist, for an emergency session. I knew I had to make some decisions for my mental health.

In less than an hour, I had an answer: I would quit surgery because I felt it was no longer rewarding. I wanted to be in control of my life. If I performed a surgery, it would be on my terms, and would enrich my soul, and not the pockets of insurance company CEOs. I decided to provide office gynecology services here in the United States, and join Dr. Charles Rene, a Haitian ob-gyn practicing in Louisiana, on his bi-annual trips to Haiti.

Don't Be Afraid to Ask for Help

While I was in New York promoting my book *Natural Pregnancy A-Z*, I started to experience severe panic attacks. I don't know how I found the courage to fly back from New York to Chicago, then to San Diego. I waited so long to board the plane I almost missed the flight! I tried to focus on the people around me, making trivial conversation and trying not to think about where I was. I tried meditation, but too many things were competing in my head. I was glad to see my husband, Albert, waiting for me at the airport in San Diego. I felt much better, perhaps because I was again in familiar surroundings, but the attack greatly disturbed me.

Through the years I have helped many women with personal problems, but now it was time to follow my own advice, time for the physician to "heal thyself." I knew that some drastic changes had to occur in my life. That was when I knew I had to get help.

"Seeking help is a sign of strength and a willingness to grow."
—Louise L. Hay

"When a woman heals herself, she heals a family, a community, and eventually, the world."
—Susan Powter

A survey conducted by the American Psychological Association in 1996 revealed that 84% of Americans feel psychological health is important for overall good health, but 47% did not know *when* it was appropriate to see a mental health professional, and 68% did not know how to *find* a mental health professional.

When women feel overwhelmed and ask for help they are often told they are being selfish. People around them play with their guilt. Black women, more than white women, are expected to be strong and to take care of the "whole race." Your mind must allow "tune ups" when it is overwhelmed or if you feel depressed. For me, it is just like taking my car to the mechanic or calling my computer guru when something goes wrong with my computer.

I continue to work with my therapists to learn how to confront my demons, and learn coping skills to serve me for the rest of my life. While browsing at a bookstore, a book caught my eye: *The Anxiety & Phobia Work-*

book, by Daniel J. Bourne. Something told me to get it. I could not have found a better book. *You Can Heal Your Life*, by Louise Hay was another book that I discovered. These books, and others, became mental health "help tools."

The following is a compilation of what I learned and practice. I have a great life, and can really say that I have found secrets to keep it in balance. Many times I am confronted with a problem that puts me off kilter. If I follow my own advice, balance is soon found again.

Coping Skills

Learn to set priorities, and only do what is most important. Find the time to do something for yourself – without feeling guilty. Some women find it difficult to relax, especially if they have a busy lifestyle and small children. Women are often caregivers to husbands, children, parents, and relatives. Who is last in line for receiving attention and nurturing? Women. I suggest that my patients try to see themselves as a battery that needs to be recharged from time to time. If it doesn't get recharged, the battery (like the woman) runs out of power just when it's needed most. Stop feeling guilty when you tell others that you cannot do what they ask.

Emotional Health

Are you frequently hijacked by your emotions? Keeping distressing emotions and impulses in check is necessary for stability and well being. Intense, extreme emotions experienced for too long undermine stability. Up and down moods are to be expected but need to be basically in balance.

Managing emotions is a full-time job – no time off! Excessive emotionalism is often a sign that a person is making an attempt to conceal weakness. We may not have much control over when we are swept up by emotion, but we have some say in *how long* an emotion will last. When they last past an appropriate time, distressing, unregulated emotions become rage, chronic anxiety and depression.

Emotions are the "body's mind." Studies show that emotions have a powerful effect on the autonomic nervous system and subsequently the immune system. Just as the rational thinking brain manages our emotions, emotions guide moment to moment decisions and can win out over rational thought.

Women's heart rates are normally about 82 beats per minute, and men's about 72 beats per minute. In times of emotional distress, the body pumps adrenaline and other hormones that keep the distress high, affecting rational thinking and creating toxic feelings that take a long time to get over. We send emotional signals in every exchange with another person, and emotions pass from one person to another – "emotional contagion!" Emotion usually passes from the more forceful personality to the more passive or sensitive personality. So, remember you can send and receive feelings, emotions and moods – both positive and negative. Better control over run-away emotion is a skill to be mastered.

Dealing With Fears

"FEAR: False Evidence Appearing Real"

Fear can short-circuit mental health in a flash. I did not like the way I felt when I was in constant fear of having another panic attack. I learned that the *fear* of another attack was *worse* than the attack, and that this fear can actually trigger it.

My panic attack occurred on a Tuesday in New York. I was there to lead a seminar at Wainwright House by the Hudson on Wednesday, then return home to San Diego on Friday. I was contemplating becoming an advisory board member for GE Center for Financial Learning. An interview with Tom Topinka, Vice President, GE Corporate Communications was added to my schedule for Monday in Manhattan. I would be the only physician in a group of highly successful financial people.

I could not sleep the night before knowing that I had to cope with the Midtown tunnel, elevators, an interview, a tight schedule and then flying back to San Diego. How could I accomplish all of this when I was fearful of sitting in a car with the windows closed? Fear was making me feel more panic. I wished I could have found Scotty to beam me up.

There was no way to get to Manhattan and be on time for the meeting without going through the dreaded Midtown tunnel. I did not want to take medication and have to deal with unexpected side effects during an interview. I was so afraid that I almost canceled the meetings. But I couldn't because Tom was flying from Philadelphia specifically to meet with me.

    I decided to try a mantra that Louise Hay uses: "All is well…all is well…all is well." I continued chanting this while in the tunnel and in the elevator and it helped. The meeting was taking place at the headquarters of Peppercom Communications, a marketing firm for GE. Meggan Lennon was there to greet me with the unfortunate news that Tom's plane had been delayed for one hour. I looked around and found myself in a nice conference room with soft lights – but no windows! I wanted to see the sun and huge wide-open windows. How was I going to last in an enclosed room, then the elevators, the tunnel, and the planes again?

    The longer I stayed in that room, the more I felt that I was going to suffer a panic attack. I wanted to run but my mind said no. That was when I tried self-hypnosis. Meggan, a very beautiful young lady with a gorgeous smile and big brown eyes, tried to entertain me. I kept focusing on her eyes, trying to forget my surroundings. After what felt like an eternity, Tom finally appeared and was happy to meet me, "A physician who has a holistic approach to health. What a delight." No one guessed the turmoil going on in my head. The interview went well and I got the position on GE's advisory board, which is quite an honor. All the way back home I chanted …all is well…all is well…all is well….

Maybe it was my medical training that helped give me strength to power through those overwhelming fears – but I believe that each one of us can find that strength. We must reach down *deep* to find it. Consciously focusing your mind on something pleasant, and even chanting, might help. Serenity is a skill you can learn to combat fears.

You Have Choices

    I have known many women living in abusive situations who felt helpless because they thought they had no choice. It may be difficult to assert ourselves and choose what is good for us, but we have to realize that we do have choices. And if we believe that we don't, then someone else will make your choices for you. The only things you cannot choose are the country of your birth, your parents, your gender, race, and physical appearance. Anything else that happens to you is by your choice, whether conscious or unconscious.

Often, when we feel helpless and out of control, we try to change the status quo. This usually brings us more stress about making a wrong decision. I, too, have found myself in situations where my stress was experienced as mental and physical pain. If I dared to think about getting out, I experienced anxiety. Many of us do not change because we do not feel strong enough to tackle it. I have seen many patients who feel "stuck." I could turn blue trying to explain that there is always a way out of any situation. We only need to be conscious that we don't like where we are and want to change. So, when you find yourself in a situation that feels like there is no way out, take the time to find out why you are in this particular situation, use your clever mind to figure out how to get out of it, and then take action.

Dealing with Change

"I am in the process of making major changes in my life, that's okay. It's safe for me to change, and I grow and prosper as a result."
—Louise L. Hay

The only thing constant in this life is *change*. If we *know* that something is no good for us, we have to change. We have to let it go.

I did not know how difficult it would be to go through a midlife change until I decided it was time to cut my hair. I've mentioned I had always been unhappy with my kinky dark brown hair and envied those who had straight hair. I spent many long hours at the hairdressers, having my hair straightened and colored. During my evaluation of this personal dilemma, I realized how difficult it is for people to change. Whether we find ourselves with a bad habit such as smoking or a drug problem, in an abusive relationship, or in an un-fulfilling job – we stay in bad situations because we are not strong enough to change, or we are afraid to deal with the *unknown*.

Taking the first step to change something is the most difficult. A friend, Juliana, put it this way: "It's like sitting on the edge of a cliff with a rabid dog running towards you, but you are afraid to jump. When you look down at the raging waters below, you don't know whether you'll break your neck or make it safely to the other side. You're frozen on the ledge, even though you know that eventually you must jump."

When I finally made the decision to cut my hair, my hairdresser, Francoise, argued against it. So, be prepared – Not only do you have to deal with your fears in making the decision to "jump," you must also deal with others who urge you *not* to change.

Dealing With Disappointments

A major life lesson I have learned so far is that when you expect something to happen and it does not, there's no need to worry – *it most likely was not supposed to happen*. The fact that it did not happen gave you experiences traveling down a different path that otherwise you would have missed.

- There is no way that we can completely avoid disappointments. A better way to act is to learn how to deal with them when they occur. Dare to dream big, knowing that not all dreams are going to be fulfilled.

- When we are disappointed in a major way we usually go through the stages of grief, which includes shock, denial, fierce anger, and sorrow. It doesn't help when someone says "don't worry, you'll be okay." The fact is, we can be surprised at how much it hurts. It's like having something accidentally fall on our toes – We know that we should feel better in a few minutes, but there is nothing we can do to make the pain vanish. We just have to get through it. But we cannot *get stuck in disappointment*; we have to move on.

- There are some things that we can control and others that we cannot.
  I studied and worked hard to become a doctor and a specialist. After many years, things were changing in the medical profession. Managed care set in. How good I was did not matter any longer. Of course I was disappointed and even disillusioned. But I had to realize that there was no way I personally could control the wave of change that was happening. I had to handle my disappointment and fall back on what I wanted when I decided to become a doctor – which was to care for those in need and teach them how to empower themselves in all aspects of their lives. So

I became a writer, and through my writing I am accomplishing my same goals, but in a different way. If I had enjoyed a successful medical practice as I planned it, this book, the ones already written, and those to be written, would not have happened. Only a few patients would have had a chance to see me on a one-on-one basis at my office. But with my books, seminars and Internet presence, I am reaching millions all over the world, beyond my wildest dreams.

Dealing With Regrets

"Regret is the cancer of life."

I know too many people who spend so much time dwelling on the past that the present passes them by – ruining the chance to create a better future. One of them, unfortunately, was my mother. I never saw her happy. She never forgave herself, until the day she died, that she did not have the means to raise me and my sister. I was a dutiful daughter who took care of her till the end and tried to do everything to make her smile. But her smile never lasted for long. I told her many times that because of her sacrifices I became motivated to take charge of my life and was able to get an education. But her regret ate at her anyway.

If you are someone cursed with regrets, here are some thoughts to consider:

- *You cannot change the past.* What is done is done. You cannot turn back the clock and change anything in the past, no matter how much you regret it.
- All we have is the *present.* This is where the action is, so "be here now." Start fresh, start over. *"Every day is the first day of the rest of..."*
- If you regret something, you must forgive yourself. Tell yourself that you did not know any better at the time. We all make foolish mistakes and they are part of the learning curve of life.
- Regret is a toxic emotion that affects your personality, and affects the people in your life. Preoccupation with regret hijacks your emotions and

interferes with focusing on the positive.
- Learn from your mistakes. The worst that could happen is that you never learn from the past and repeat the same mistake again and again – a cycle that keeps you in an endless loop of regret.

Creative Visualization

Creative visualization literally means that you create a visual image in your mind of a positive outcome. Whenever I felt discouraged during my medical training I would picture myself holding the first baby I would deliver in private practice - a little girl wearing a pink dress. That image represented something tangible as a goal. It sustained me when everything seemed hopeless. It represented the prize for all my efforts. For you, your efforts may be to provide for and support the needs of your family. Your prize may be the vision of a happy, healthy family, seated around a table, eating a good meal. (By the way, the first baby I delivered in my private practice in San Diego on April 21, 1983, was, indeed, a little girl.)

There are many hard things that we must endure to reach a goal. A couple of examples include completing college courses to earn a degree, or taking an extra job to pay unexpected bills. Regardless of the situation, keeping a re-"mind"-er that it is only temporary can make it less stressful. And creatively envisioning the *end result* in your mind may help you to plow through difficult times.

"The Sky's the Limit"

There's a special saying or "mantra" I'd like to share with you, and I'll tell you why…Before I started traveling back to Haiti to do volunteer work, I spent time with some special children in the San Diego community. I "adopted" the St. Stephen's Christian School of mostly black children K1 - 12, led by Bishop George McKinney and his wife. I fell in love with the children in their school uniforms. When I looked at their bright faces, I saw myself in every one of them.

Once a month, I would spend a whole morning at the school. We gathered first for one hour in the church so all the grades could fit in, and we would start with one student coming in front of the class to recite something I taught them: *"The sky is the limit. I can be anything that I want to be if I work hard for it."* All the children would repeat it proudly. Then we would discuss a motivating topic. The rest of the morning I spent with grades 9 through 12 to answer questions about a chosen topic or to talk about anything they wanted to address.

Now, years later, it gives me such a good feeling when a young lady or gentleman unexpectedly approaches me in the supermarket or somewhere else and with a big smile says, *"The sky is the limit. I can be anything that I want to be if I work hard for it."* They tell me that they had never forgotten the mantra and that because they took it to heart, they are doing well in life. Many of these children, now in college, or in postgraduate school, have parents who never graduated from high school.

What a profound influence we can have on self-esteem with positive motivation. I told these children that they should *"dare to dream big."* That the only barriers they could not overcome were those that they placed in front of themselves. I told them to dare dream big because of my own experience: That it would not matter whether they were black, or female, as long as words like honesty, integrity, character, goals and hard work were part of their vocabulary. That they should never settle for anything small. That they should buck the status quo, ignore prejudice and keep motivating themselves – that they could be doctors, lawyers, teachers, president of this country. The sky's the limit!

And I specifically told those children that they should never worry about statistics or people who say to those who dare dream big that "it's impossible to do something because no one else like them had ever done such a thing." I told them about my own story – that in Haiti when I decided to become a doctor, I had *never seen a woman doctor before.* That when I decided to come to San Diego because I loved the weather, I was told that I could never make it because people were prejudiced and I could never have a successful practice as a black woman doctor. And the list of negatives would go on and on!

The other day, I was talking to Durelene, a sweet 16-year-old girl whom I've invited to spend the weekends with me. She was born in Haiti, her parents and her many siblings came to this country as refugees when she was 9 years old and they all live a modest life. I promised that she could spend as much time as she wanted with me.

I would offer the refuge I wished I had when I was her age and felt that I belonged nowhere. I call her "my weekend daughter."

The first time we spent the weekend together, we were talking about her dreams, and she told me that she want to be a lawyer but feared that she may not be able to make it because she's a woman and she's black. My answer to that was that the only thing she could not be in this country was the president. And not because she is a woman or black, but only because in the US constitution a foreign-born person cannot become president. When I saw the light of hope in her eyes, I knew we were on the right track to reach her self-esteem.

Keep a Journal

The first time I saw my therapist, she gave me a journal to write in as part of my homework. Keeping a journal forces you to open your mind and find out what is going on within you. I wrote down everything that was bothering me. Seeing it on paper helps you to view your problems more clearly, especially if you are a visual person like I am. Sometimes writing things down puts them in perspective. Compiling a list of possible options for each problem or challenge creates an action plan.

Hobbies

Having a hobby – and I mean a healthy one – is enriching and keeps your mind and your life balanced. Take a class, learn to play an instrument, just do whatever it is that you've "put on the back burner until later when blah, blah, blah...."

One day a patient came to see me fearing that something was "wrong" with her, but she could not pinpoint what it was. She had been my patient for many years; I delivered her two children, now ages 16 and 14. I knew that she had been a good stay-home mom, taking the kids everywhere and supporting them in everything they wished to do. I remembered that she used to love to sing in a choir, but she said she had no time anymore for choir practice. I examined her and sent her home with a written prescription: "Choir practice weekly." I told her that she *had to find the time to go to choir prac-*

tice. She was ordered to call me in a month. She called three weeks later. She had gone back to choir practice and was feeling *much* better.

My sister Elsie at age 44 found a small lump in her right breast. Her mammogram and an ultrasound were negative. There is no history of cancer in our family. A fine needle biopsy was negative.

Elsie did not like having a lump in her breast, so she asked for a referral and to have it removed. It was cancer, after all, and it was micro-invasive. She was given the option of mastectomy or lumpectomy, and the lymph nodes under her armpit would have to be removed. She opted for the lumpectomy. Bad news again: a few cancer cells were left behind. Elsie would have to return for a mastectomy.

Elsie promised herself that she would learn the saxophone if she made it through her latest ordeal. Why the saxophone? Because when she was 12, she had admired a girl playing the saxophone in a high school band in Haiti. It was unusual for a girl to go to school back then, no less to play the saxophone. Elsie survived her many surgeries and took up saxophone lessons to cope with her stress. Playing the saxophone became *so rewarding* for Elsie that she joined Nancy's Prince of Peace church band.

Take Time to Shed Tears

Dealing with stress is hard for women, and can be even harder for men. It's okay for a woman to cry, to admit something is wrong, find solace with a friend, or seek professional help. Society makes it difficult for men to allow themselves do these things. "Men don't cry," they say. Fortunately, since September 11th, our point of view is beginning to shift. We all cried with the men on TV at Ground Zero in New York.

Crying releases toxins from the body. When toxins collect in the body over a period of time, they can cause illness. Many illnesses are now being recognized as the result of emotions that have been ignored for years.

Glen Dawdson, MD, studied the effects of tears because he believed they were important to the healing process. In his study, participants who wept openly and freely after the death of a spouse recovered from the grief and depression at a much faster rate than those who did not. So, when you feel overwhelmed, let the tears flow.

I always feel better after a good cry. Sometimes I cry in situations that previously would have caused me shame. Now I cry when I feel like it. Over the years crying has helped me many times as I confronted a painful situation. It seems that crying gives me a chance to feel sorry for myself, and the tears release my sense of helplessness. So I strongly recommend that you try this beneficial, and *free*, remedy.

Role Models

Wouldn't it have been ideal to have a wise, inspiring role model when you were a child, and more role models while you were growing up? You may say that because you were raised in a dysfunctional family you had no role models – there was no one around or successful, etc., but that's no excuse. No matter your age, it is never too late to find a role model or two.

There have been many men and women who have inspired me. I will describe a few of the role models who have made a profound impact on me, especially during the past few years during my search for *myself.* They have inspired me and will continue to do so all my life. Some I have never even met. Perhaps they may inspire you too.

• Grandma

My grandmother Eugenie Jean was born in a little town in northern Haiti called Anse Rouge. While she only had two years of schooling, she was one of the wisest women I have ever met. I went to live with her when I was very young because my mother was too poor to raise me. Grandma taught me about respecting myself and others, about giving, letting go, about caring, about being a healer, how I could become anything I dreamed, and about unconditional love.

Among the many important things I learned from Grandma was that it is never too late to learn. She was 64 years old and was traveling to America to visit my father. She sheepishly approached me to confess that she did not know how to write. She bought a notebook and wanted to learn how to sign her name. She did not want to use a cross as her signature any longer, especially in her passport. I was shocked to learn her well-kept secret, but I was proud of her for trying.

In her notebook, I wrote her name, each letter on one line. I watched her struggle for days trying to write with her arthritic hands. When her passport finally arrived, I saw the pride in her eyes when she sat down and slowly but legibly signed her name.

- **My Sister Marise**

Marise and I grew up together. Grandma taught us the virtue of telling the truth and to be afraid of no one. My medical training also taught me to be self-assured and assertive. I was never afraid to speak my mind *at any time* and I do not think twice about it. This was also a defense mechanism developed as the result of living in a world where I needed to speak up as a black and as a woman.

Marise has always been soft spoken; she could speak her mind but I always felt she was a wimp. It took some time but eventually I realized that secretly I had always admired her patience and her gentle ways with people. Now, I am much better with people. I talk to Marise often; although I am close to my other brothers and sisters, I share a special bond with her. I consult her whenever I make a major decision, especially when other people's feelings are involved. I consider her my best friend.

- **Hinda J. Larkey**

I call her my "adopted Jewish mother." Hinda was the first American person with whom I developed a close bond. I met her during my residency training in Milwaukee. Her husband Jay Larkey, MD, was the head of obstetrics at Mount Sinai Medical Center. They have two daughters Cindy and Debbie, and a son Hirsh. They were my adopted Jewish family. I teased that I was "their daughter the doctor." When Debbie decided to go to medical school and later chose to be an ob-gyn, I always reminded her that I was the first in the family.

Hinda reminded me of Grandma. She taught me never to compromise, and to stand for what I believed was right. She was very outspoken. The first time I went to her home, she proudly showed me the wall of pictures and newspaper clippings devoted to her role in the civil rights movement. She had been arrested many times. Black civil rights activists always had a room in her home since they could not get a room in the hotels.

One day, Hinda visited me in San Diego. My Grandma was staying with me at that time. She and Hinda shared an instant spiritual connection. This was strange since Hinda spoke no Haitian or French and Grandma spoke no English. I loved her for that. The last time I saw her was at a family reunion in Milwaukee in 1996. Hinda died the following spring. According to her religion she was buried the next day, so I did not get the chance to go. I was glad that I had the opportunity to tell her how much I loved her when she was alive.

- **Christiane Northrup, MD**

In 1997, I was in professional turmoil. I knew I did not want to continue to practice medicine the way I had been doing it in San Diego. With managed care defining doctor-patient relationships, I was becoming more and more disenchanted with medicine. Then I met Christiane.

I had not heard of her before, nor had I read her best-selling book *Women's Bodies, Women's Wisdom.* Her marketing literature was arriving in women's mailboxes in San Diego, telling them not to accept "one-size fits all" medicine. When I heard she was coming to San Diego for a four-day seminar, I decided to attend. I did not go to learn from her, as I felt we had the same credentials. What could she teach me? I believed that I wanted to "spy" on her – to check her out.

At first, I was incognito in the crowd. Eventually, after hearing her, I admitted I was there to learn from her. I learned that you had to have the courage to stand for your beliefs, especially when it's about the way you want to treat your patients. You have to find the strength to get out of the rat race of managed care and stand up against the status quo. In 1985, long before alternative healing was in vogue, Christiane took that step.

From Christiane, I learned I was right not to want to practice medicine through managed care, that everything I learned about listening to your own body, making a patient part of the treatment process, accepting alternative medicine as well as the Western approach to medicine, was okay.

I also learned that you can be a powerful person and be empowering. When you *know* that you come from a world of plenty, you are not afraid to openly share with others; you are not afraid that the well will run dry. I became empowered after that conference.

- **Louise L. Hay**

Louise attended part of Christiane's seminar. She heard some of my comments and decided to meet me. It was an instant soul connection. I had not heard of her until that day. Her books, especially *You Can Heal Your Life,* have inspired millions. Louise became a mentor, a friend, and a patient. With her financial help, I have been able to provide much needed surgical care to poor women. She is a strong supporter of my Haiti project scholarships through which 200 destitute children are educated each year.

Louise also publishes calendars with daily affirmations. It seems that whenever I am troubled, the calendars provide the exact message I need to hear from her. Through her writings, Louise is the equivalent of Grandma to me. I tried to explain it to her once but could not find the right words. She just kissed me and said: "I love you too."

- **Maya Angelou**

I have never met Maya Angelou, but often read about her. The first time I got a glimpse of her was when she read a poem on television at President Clinton's inauguration. I was in the process of recording an audio-tape and my assistant, David, suggested I practice imitating someone whose voice I liked. I bought *The Maya Angelou Poetry Collection.* I enjoyed her writing, and listening to her helped my diction and pace.

When I had to make the difficult decision to quit private practice after 19 years, Maya's wisdom came to the rescue. I closed my office, not knowing what I was going to do when I returned from a missionary trip to Haiti. The airline's in-flight magazine had Maya's picture on the cover with the inscription, "Maya Angelou: A Caged Bird No Longer." Jane Ammeson interviewed her. The first thing to catch my attention was a quote: "I wanted to say to young people, 'Look. Be where you are. And if you don't like it, make some changes'."

As I read the interview, I discovered that she and I have a lot in common. We both speak several languages. Her grandmother raised her in rural segregated Stamps, Arkansas. Maya read avidly, books selected by her grandmother, just as I did. Just like my Grandma, her grandmother was a woman of vision. Her grandmother told her: "If you walk up a path that somebody else told you to walk, and you look ahead and you don't like where you're going, and you look back and you don't want to return, step off the path. Pick yourself a brand new road." I cried; I was glad I was seated in a window seat. I lay my head against the window and wept while watching clouds fly by. For the first time in many years my future was uncertain, but I knew that I had made the right choice about changing my path.

- **Charles Rene, MD**

I met Charles in 1989. He was an ob-gyn with a private practice in New Orleans. He asked me to join his team of health-care workers who travel to La Vallee de Jacmel, Haiti, twice a year to provide free medical care. On these charitable visits, they provide outpatient care, minor surgery, and when permitted, emergency C-sections. The team helps an average of 150 patients per day, putting in long days of 12 hours or more. There is a single non-sterile operating room without adequate supplies, therefore, only minor surgeries under local/regional anesthesia can be performed. A generator provides electricity, but only when there is gas. Often, surgery is performed with an assistant holding a flashlight while a citronella candle wards off mosquitoes and flies.

During my "search for myself," I returned to Haiti several times, often attempting to do volunteer medical work, in addition to the money I often sent to help those in need. Charles asked me to go with his group of medical missionaries, but I put it off. I realized that I believed that I could not join Charles and the others because I just did not have enough guts to do it.

One day the answer came to me, although I am not sure how. The message was clear: It's time to go home to use the skills I had acquired through the years. I knew that the conditions would be horrible, but that it was the right thing to do. Before, I had always let my fear talk me out of going. This time, when fear tried to take over, it was met with: "Avas ou tu veux, meurs ou tu dois." "Go where you must, die where you have to." I so admire Charles for doing this for years.

- **Professor Aubies Franck**

Heroes and role models may be found in unexpected places. One of my heroes, Professor Aubies Franck, resides in La Vallee de Jacmel, a small town overlooking the Caribbean Sea, high in the mountains of southwestern Haiti.

While growing up, my dream was to build a hospital to provide medical care for the poor in Haiti. Once I grew tired of American medicine, the message became so clear: It's time for me to go home! Although it wasn't time to build my own hospital, it was time to join Dr. Charles Rene and his medical missionaries on his 20th trip to Haiti.

How can I explain what I felt when we finally landed? Once I set foot on Haitian soil, it was like being reborn. "I am home." Even though I had been away for a long time, the surroundings looked very familiar. I saw my grandmother, my mother, my family, even myself, in the face of everyone I saw. It was as though I had never left. I felt connected with an old lady with a faint smile, a young boy reminded me of my little brother. We were all one big family.

The crowds, the dust, the poverty did not matter. It didn't matter that there wasn't hot water for a shower. It didn't matter that electricity was available only from 6 to 9 PM, that every meal had to be made from scratch and cooked on a charcoal stove, that water only trickled from the tap, and there was no refrigerator or microwave. At the hotel in Jacmel I could take a hot shower, but was dive-bombed by mosquitoes everywhere I went.

That was when I met Professor Aubies Franck, a soft-spoken gentleman in his 70's, and the president of CODEVA (Coude-a-Coude Pour le Development de La Vallee). In 1975, La Vallee was cut off from the rest of the country because of bad road conditions and CODEVA was created. There were no health-care programs, hospitals, schools for the poor, educational programs, electricity, telephones, drinkable water, or technical assistance for agricultural needs. The people of La Vallee worked to improve the roads, re-plant the forest, built a small hospital, three primary schools, a secondary school, and a public market. This community effort came with a price: Professor Aubies and other leaders were tortured and jailed for wanting to bring change.

The first thing I noticed upon visiting his home was a large poster written in Haitian:

> Fe tout byen ou kapab
> Tout tan ou kapab
> Tout jan ou kapab
> Tout Kote ou kapab
> Pou tout moun ou kapab
> Jouk tan ou pa kapab anko

Do as much good as you can
As long as you can
Any way you can
Wherever you can
For anyone you can
Until you no longer can

"We really mean it," said his wife who saw me reading the poster. "Many times we would go without to help a child go to school or to buy medications for a sick child."

I believe that to make things work, especially in a foreign country, one must determine the needs of the people and work with these people to achieve their goals. So I listened to Professor Aubies.

"First of all, I would like to feed the children who have to come hungry to school after walking for hours. Since it is not possible, we could teach them music." Why music? "Because when you teach children music, you elevate their souls, give them something to do after class, as well as give them the opportunity to make a living in the future." Professor Aubies asked me follow him. We entered another room where he pulled a bunch of sheet music from a large cabinet. "I have been hoping one day to have a school band. But there is no money to buy instruments or to pay the music teachers."

From another drawer, he pulled an architectural design. "We have already bought the land," he said. "This is the plan for a building where we will have a vocational school and a hospitality home for those who come to help teach the children and take care of the sick at the hospital. Our children have nothing to do with book education. After finishing school in La Vallee, the children must leave, and many die in the slums of Port-au-Prince or drown in flimsy boats."

What an inspiration this dear man was for me to create "Angels for Haiti," a non-profit charitable foundation to help improve life over there.

- **Gary Guy Moreau**

My mother passed away on September 25th in Miami, Florida, just a few hours after I had whispered "I love you" in her ear over the phone. Marise, Elsie, and her husband, Guy, bore the brunt of her care as the rest of the family lived in other parts of the country.

A little more than a month later, Guy was struck by a vehicle as he stood by his car, stalled on the Palmetto Freeway. The car burst into flames, trapping him underneath. At the risk of being killed, strangers who saw the accident lifted the car and pulled him out. He was airlifted to the burn unit at Jackson Memorial Hospital, unconscious. The right side of his head, face, neck, arm and upper chest were severely burned. He was not supposed to live.

Guy regained consciousness on December 16th. He had lost all of the fingers on his right hand, two on the left. His right arm was grafted and locked at the elbow. His left arm was atrophied and also locked at the elbow. Those who saw the right side of his body said he looked like a monster. Everything had to be done for him. My siblings and I spent most of our time consoling Elsie and traveling back and forth to the Jackson Memorial Hospital Burn Unit, miles away from where we lived.

Guy, who had been a handsome man, was now skin and bones and badly disfigured. At first we thought that he had sustained brain damage, or had lost most of his vision, since he always greeted us with a smile and never complained. I soon realized that Guy was aware of everything that had happened. He told me, and the rest of the family, not to worry – that he was going to be okay. Other people who he met during his physical therapy sessions were not as fortunate in his eyes: they were blind, paraplegic, quadriplegic, unable to speak, or were mentally retarded. He said he believed in God and looked forward to learning the reason his life had been spared.

On New Year's Eve, Guy and I sat together. The television was on. A commercial aired featuring Christopher Reeve seated in his wheelchair and kept alive by a machine. "See!" Guy said, "He has accepted what happened to him. So do I." Before I left him that evening, he also told me that since his wife did not like pain, and he loved her too much to let her see him suffering, he decided that *he would just have to be strong enough for the both of them.*

Guy finally went home on February 11th and on February 14th he sent me an e-mail: "May the beauty of this day bring you love and joy!" Guy has had to undergo many surgeries since his release. He postponed additional, but necessary, surgeries when Elsie discovered a lump in her breast two months later, which turned out to be cancer. Then a hurricane struck and their house flooded. Over the telephone Guy was as cheerful as ever, "Don't worry, everything will be okay!" So, whenever I feel overwhelmed, I think of Guy. Seeing him, talking to him or just thinking of his strength of character, keeps my mind strong. He received his Masters degree in Information Technology in June, 2002.

- **Some of my teachers during my medical training stand out as inspiring role models:**

Ms. Dickenson, a labor and delivery nurse at Cornwall Regional Hospital in Jamaica, taught me that pregnancy and childbirth were natural - that if given enough time during labor, a woman would deliver vaginally, and there was no need for an episiotomy. During my residency at Mount Sinai Medical Center in Milwaukee, Dr. Maurice Sable, Dr. Allen Babbitz, my adopted dad Dr. Jay Larkey, and Dr. Fredrik Broekhuizen, each taught me how to take extra special care of my patients.

So you see, people you know, and those even far away, can inspire you. If you are confronted with a situation that you want to improve, stop and list the qualities you admire in someone who you look up to, dead or alive, near or far, and see what you can learn from them.

Stress In Our Lives

The word "stress" has become very commonly used, as if it is a normal byproduct of the demands of life. Stress is the effect that these demands have on our mind, and our body. It's what Mother Nature built into us way back in evolutionary time to prepare us to meet and survive the unexpected. It is meant to induce the "fight or flight" response, to allow us to overpower our enemies or to escape. When we react to something we perceive as danger, our body pumps out a series of hormones that make us more alert and ready to act.

Acute stress affects the autonomic nervous system. Heart rate increases, pupils dilate, blood rushes toward large muscles and away from the fingers and toes. Muscles can tighten and adrenaline and cortisol are released into the blood stream. If we act on these signals with our physical body, by running or fighting, this excess energy is used.

In modern society, stress confronts us at work and at home, but not in the form of a lurking saber-toothed tiger. So our body's "alert" is turned in other directions. Sometimes we exercise, running to "chill out." If we can't move about, stress keeps pumping the hormones into our bloodstream until they assault our blood vessels, our heart, our immune system and our liver. You can't eliminate stress from your life. In fact, you don't really want to. Some stress helps you focus your energies, sort your priorities, make decisions, and perform better. The secret is to know how to control stress. People who don't know how to control stress in a positive manner often use unhealthy alternatives like drinking, smoking, drug abuse, or overwork. Stress can also lead people to mentally or physically abuse their children or spouse. It's even linked to motor-vehicle accidents.

We become stressed when we realize that we are in a situation that is out of our control, or when we cannot see the light at the end of the tunnel. Most situations have a beginning, a middle, and an end, whether we believe this or not. How long we stay in a horrible situation is up to us. The stress status quo is what can kill us.

Many of my patients report physical symptoms such as irregular bleeding, difficulty sleeping or the fact that they are no longer responding to medications that have been successful in the past. Invariably, these people are experiencing stress, whether it is emotional or financial, work-related or not.

There are two types of stress: negative and positive. The difference between the two depends upon whether you feel you are in *control* of the stress. Some stress helps you to focus your energies, sort your priorities, make decisions, and perform better–this is positive stress. Negative stress occurs when you feel a lack of control in a particular situation.

Negative stress is what invariably happens to women. Women are less prone to be in positions of power and to have control over what happens in their lives. Women also tend to take care of everyone else's needs before taking care of their own. I have diagnosed cancer far too many times in women who sought my medical help for symptoms long after the symptoms started. These women were too busy caring for others, an elderly parent, a sick spouse, or children, to stop and take care of their own needs. Women are also expected to perform multiple tasks and duties. They often hold full-time jobs in addition to maintaining a household. Women may speak up and complain that the husband or the teenager does not help. Why should they? They know that she will complain a little and then do the task herself! When I ask women why they continue to do these things, they don't know why; they feel they have to and are unaware of their own stress and resentment.

It is normal for everyone to experience stress; in fact, it's inevitable. Some of life's occurrences normally produce stress. Exercise is a form of good stress. That keyed-up feeling, often referred to as "stage fright," occurs before you give a performance or a speech. You're nervous – but properly controlled, the feeling gives extra energy to your efforts. New experiences, like buying a new house, moving across the country, or taking a new job, are stressful. Bad stress includes things like overwork or the death of a relative.

Take the Stress Questionnaire

Are you experiencing any of the following?

- Absence of menses (if you are not menopausal)
- Anxiety attack
- Chronic fatigue
- Diminished response to a prescribed medication
- Excessive heartburn
- Forgetfulness
- Gastritis
- Hot flashes
- Inability to concentrate
- Insomnia
- Irregular heartbeat after a period of stress
- Irregular menses
- Irritable bowel
- Lack of appetite, or overeating
- Loss of hair (alopecia areata)
- Loss of sexual desire
- Mouth ulcers
- Muscle spasms
- Nightmares
- Skin disorders
- Stomach or duodenal
- Teeth grinding
- Tension headaches
- Trembling or shaking
- Trouble falling asleep
- Ulcerative colitis
- Ulcers

The more symptoms you own, the more likely you are to suffer from stress. You need to learn to better cope with the situations that produce these results, or you will continue to suffer the consequences.

Be aware of these unsuspected causes of stress:

- Marriage
- Divorce
- Giving birth
- Children moving away from home
- Changes in partners
- A chronic illness (or a partner with one)
- Shift in financial status
- Changing or losing a job
- Death of a family member or friend
- Moving
- Selling or buying a home
- Catastrophic event, such as what occurred on September 11th 2001
- Fear of terrorist attacks

Unresolved stress causes the continual release of hormones into the bloodstream. These hormones assault the blood vessels, heart, immune system, and liver. The end result is problems such as high blood pressure, increased susceptibility to illness, viral and bacterial infections, ulcers, headaches, chronic muscular tension, high cholesterol levels, heart attacks, hormonal imbalance, and even cancer. Women who are stressed are more likely to suffer from the common cold. Some women tend to develop eating disorders such as anorexia, bulimia, or overeating. They may have a tendency to abuse illicit or prescription drugs, alcohol, and cigarettes. Some women, who previously quit smoking, may resume the habit at this time. Women who are under a lot of stress are more likely to experience stress-related illnesses and may be more prone to accidental injuries. They may perform poorly at work and tend to be involved in more interpersonal problems, family conflicts, and social isolation.

Learn to listen to your *own* body. Negative feelings and/or bodily symptoms that we experience are warning signs that we should let go or change situations or people in our lives.

Tips to sabotage stress:

- Go to a retreat: Leave everything behind, intimate partner, children, and relatives. See yourself as a battery that needs to be recharged from time to time. Otherwise, it will run out of power just when it's needed most.
- Try relaxation techniques such as meditation, progressive muscle relaxation, stretching, guided visual imagery, biofeedback, yoga, and prayer.
- Listen to relaxing music. When I drive, I don't listen to the news; I play music that I enjoy.
- Get a massage. If you can't afford it, ask your friends, co-workers, children, or partner to buy you one for your next birthday or holiday.
- Join a self-help support group. Self-help groups offer a place to meet regularly and share experiences, and help you feel less alone.
- Get an adequate amount of sleep each night.
- Exercise!
- Discontinue bad habits, like smoking.
- Avoid stimulants such as caffeine, herbs that contain ma huang, Chinese ephedra, and illegal drugs, such as amphetamines and cocaine.
- Do not abuse alcohol.
- Herbs such as chamomile tea, passionflower, and valerian root, may help with relaxation.
- Try aromatherapy – lavender, vanilla, fennel, and valerian root calm the nervous system.
- Acupuncture treatments rebalance the body's energy meridians.
- Stop or reduce watching the television news.
- Read the newspaper headlines and only those articles that interest you.
- Maintain a clean and peaceful environment, and play soothing music at home.
- Soak in a bubble bath or whirlpool.
- Breathe. When we're stressed, we tend to take quick, shallow breaths. To reduce stress, take slow, deep breaths; inhale deeply, filling the entire diaphragm, and hold for a few seconds, then release the air gradually.
- Talk to your good friends; recovery through my midlife crisis would have taken longer if I did not have good friends to talk to.
- Take up a new hobby or join a club.

- Get an animal companion.
- Limit what must be done every day to a more reasonable list.
- Start delegating responsibilities at work and at home. Improve your time-management skills.
- Maintain a sense of humor and *laugh* - Findings from a number of studies have revealed that laughter augments immune system functioning. According to a study reported at the annual scientific sessions of the American Heart Association, possessing a good sense of humor seems to be good for our hearts. Individuals who use humor as an adaptive mechanism in difficult situations; attempt to see humor in surprise situations, daily activities, or social interactions; and those who laugh in positive situations, were less likely to suffer from heart disease.

SAD-Seasonal Affective Disorder

Who Gets SAD?

Many women experience a range of symptoms during occasional periods of the "winter blues," but when the symptoms become more "seasonal" than occasional, you may have a case of seasonal affective disorder, or SAD. Approximately 35 million Americans are affected by SAD to some degree, with at least 10 million lives seriously disrupted by its' effects.

As many as 25% of those who live in the northern regions of the United States may be SAD sufferers. The further north or south of the equator, the higher the incidence of SAD.

Seasonal Affective Disorder occurs most often in children, adolescents, and women; 75% to 80% of those affected are women usually over thirty.

Symptoms of SAD

- Lack of energy; increased fatigue, increased need for sleep, lethargy
- Increased appetite; weight gain, craving for sugar and carbohydrates
- Withdrawal; difficulty with relationships, loss of sexual desire, anxiety
- Difficulty focusing and concentrating on tasks
- Increased PMS symptoms
- Depression occurring mostly during fall and winter months

SAD is different from depression and different treatments are used. Depression usually is consistent from morning to night in severity, while SAD patients report depression and fatigue that increase in severity during the day. It's important to be sure it's SAD you are experiencing and not depression. See your physician for a diagnosis if you're experiencing any symptoms that interfere with your daily life.

What causes SAD?

- SAD is caused by the shorter days of winter and the resultant reduction of sunlight to the retina.
- There's a biological connection: the sun causes the bodys' level of serotonin to increase; lack of sunlight causes a reduction of serotonin and an increase in the level of melatonin which, in turn, causes seasonal depression.
- During a normal sleep-wake cycle the levels of serotonin and melatonin vary according to time of day, so we sleep at night and are awake during the day. If your brain chemistry is off-balance, your serotonin levels may not increase enough during the short, often cloudy days of winter.

Treatment of SAD

Seasonal Affective Disorder is often improved with the use of light therapy. The lack of light causes SAD, so increasing light to the brain, through the retina, is the effective solution for 60% to 80% of patients who have tried this therapy. Improvement is usually noted within the first four to five days of treatment. Special lamps are used with a preferred power of *10,000 lux*; the equivalent of five to twenty times the normal brightness of the lights in your home or office.

Patients are instructed to sit, in front of these lights, from 30 minutes to two hours per day. It's not necessary or recommended to look at the light; however you may read, watch TV, or do whatever you wish during exposure time.

Most patients use their lights as soon as they wake up in the morning; for some it's more effective with use at night. Some patients may also find it helpful to set an automatic timer to turn on the lamp two hours before they wake up, as a natural sunrise would occur.

Tips to Reduce SAD Symptoms

- Spend extra time outdoors on sunny days.
- Follow a low-fat diet; avoid excessive protein.
- Reduce carbohydrates and sugar.
- Taking vitamins with magnesium, B complex, and minerals may be helpful.
- Eliminate caffeine from your diet; coffee, tea, sodas, chocolate...
- Exercise activities increase levels of dopamines, plus increase your energy level.
- For milder cases try increasing your household lights.

Depression

Depression can be defined as a feeling of sadness, reduced activity, apathy, and self-deprecation. It is normal to feel sad from time to time; however, if the feeling persists for a long period of time and it's extreme, it could indicate a major physical or emotional problem that may require therapeutic intervention.

In the United States, the lifetime risk of major depression disorder among women ranges from 10 to 25%, compared with 2% to 3% for men. Each year, 20 million American adults experience a major depressive episode. Thirty-five percent of women, or one in three, experience a major depressive episode at some time over the course of their lifetime. Seventy percent of women experience mild to moderate mood and behavioral changes during their menstrual cycle, and for as many as 5% of these women, symptoms interfere with their quality of life.

Mild Depression

The symptoms of mild clinical depression include a depressed mood for most of the day for at least two years, and at least two of the following symptoms:

- Changes in appetite; eating too much or not at all
- Changes in weight

- Fatigue or lack of energy
- Difficulty concentrating, thinking, or making decisions
- Feeling guilty, worthless, or useless
- Feelings of hopelessness, helplessness, and sadness
- Sleeping problems: insomnia or oversleeping

Dealing with mild depression:

- Follow a healthy diet
- Take supplements such as vitamin B complex, folic acid, and selenium 100 mcg/day
- Regular exercise
- Relaxation techniques such as meditation, progressive muscle relaxation, yoga, and biofeedback
- Mind/body interventions
- Dance and music

Severe Depression

The symptoms of severe clinical depression include a morose mood, a loss of interest in recreational activities, jobs, hobbies, friends, and sex, plus at least *five* of the following:

- Daily sleeping problems; too much or too little sleep
- Changes in appetite: eating too much or not eating at all
- Marked changes in weight
- Feeling blue and/or disinterested
- Difficulty concentrating, thinking, or making decisions
- Feelings of hopelessness, helplessness, or sadness
- Feelings of self-reproach or guilt
- Anxiety attacks
- Fatigue or loss of energy nearly every day
- Suicidal thoughts or recurring thoughts of death

If you are severely depressed, please seek medical attention.

RELATIONSHIP WITH WORK

Work has many definitions. In this context I am talking about what you do for money. We spend nearly half of our time working. The relationship we have with our work can greatly affect our overall health. Regardless of what we do, it is important that we like what we do, and that it provides satisfaction, as well as the material compensation for which we strive.

My advice is that no one should choose a career for monetary reasons *alone*. If you choose something you love, it will not seem to be such hard work to make the money you want.

Of course, there is no perfect situation. We would like to be compensated adequately for what we do, but often we are not. Work is often stressful. As the numbers of women in leadership increase, women are faced with numerous issues: family issues, paid leave, ergonomic safety, pay equity, health-care and retirement benefits, sexual harassment, and flex-time schedules. With the current trend toward downsizing, workers are expected to do more and more.

I have many patients who do not see anything wrong with working 10 or more hour days and carrying a pager at home. These individuals erroneously believe that everything will crumble without them. In fact, the only thing that crumbles is themselves! Don't get me wrong. If you are starting a new business, or your company is going through tough times, it is okay to put in some extra hours – just do not make it your way of life. You cannot let your work run your life; you need time to share some fun with your family.

You've heard the saying, "If you love what you do, you will never work a day in your life." If you like what you do you may end up doing it for free, or at a reduced price, if you have a choice. I am fortunate to have that choice. I liked the idea of being one of the first black women doctors with a successful private practice in San Diego. I did not mind working in a clinic that served the poor, receiving a small stipend in return for my efforts. For many years, I also found or made the time to provide free medical care at the Rachel Center for the homeless, the St. Vincent de Paul Village Medical Clinic, both in San Diego, and since 1999 in La Vallee de Jacmel, Haiti. Doing volunteer work makes you wealthy in other ways than receiving money!

Many people continue to work in dead-end jobs in order to pay the bills. Some may be trying to hang on to a losing business venture because they like what they do and know of no other way around it. If these situations continue unabated, something will eventually give, leading to depression, addiction to alcohol or drugs, divorce, abusive behavior to spouse or children, heart attacks, strokes, or, in my case, severe panic attacks. The sense of hopelessness and helplessness with little control over events is the catalyst to these occurrences. If you recognize yourself here, please consider the following affirmation by Louise L. Hay:

"I charge a price for my services that is commensurate with my knowledge, experience, and abilities. All of my clients are pleased with my work. My highest purpose is to be true to myself. When I honor my personal gifts and talents, I fulfill my destiny and serve others at the same time."

If you feel that you are in a dead-end job, you are more than likely suffering stress. You may be able to change your situation by consciously doing the following:

- Try not to sweat the small stuff
- Your attitude is a choice that YOU make
- Think and behave positively
- Avoid working through lunch
- Take a walk or read during your lunch hour
- Take regular breaks
- Interact with co-workers you enjoy
- Manage your time – try not to become distracted
- Plan well and change poor planning habits
- Learn to identify your low and high peak energy levels
- Stop rushing – if you need help, ask for it
- Control your reaction to stressful situations
- Turn complaints into objectives
- Create lists – prioritize – do the essentials first
- Be realistic – don't set your goals too high
- Renew your goals often
- Take several small steps instead of large leaps
- Incorporate some quality time into your day
- If allowable, delegate duties to co-workers
- Listen to relaxing music as you work.
- Laughter often eases a tense situation

Burnout

Estimates show that 25% of workers show symptoms of burnout. Job burnout does not occur overnight. Over the years I have seen patients with persistent symptoms, such as yeast, herpes, flu, irregular bleeding, sleeping difficulties, lack of concentration, lack of energy, crying for no reason, isolation, and all because they felt stressed at work. Occasional stress in your job is not uncommon, but if abnormal situations persist without remedy, burnout will eventually occur.

Burnout Questionnaire

Please ask yourself these important questions:

- Is it hard for you to get up to go to work in the morning?
- Do you feel tired or have low energy while at work?
- Do you feel depressed when it is time to go back to work after a weekend or a vacation?
- Do you feel that you are in a dead-end situation?
- Do you feel like a failure?
- Do you feel trapped?
- Do you feel like you spend more time doing paperwork than dealing with your clients?
- Do you feel that you are overworked, underpaid?
- Do you get bored easily at work?
- Is it no longer fun at work?
- Do you feel that you are doing the work that you have to do instead of the work that you want to?
- Are you feeling resentful about your job, co-worker, boss, or the whole company?
- Are your relationships outside of your work affected by the stress you encounter at work?

The more questions you answered with a yes, the more likely you are to suffer burnout. You need to seek burnout counseling or start looking for another job, regardless of how important you feel this job is.

RELATIONSHIP WITH YOUR PARTNER

> *"The person in my life who presents the greatest challenge is also giving me the chance to understand, forgive and send love unconditionally."*
> —Louise L. Hay

Compelling evidence indicates that both men and women experience substantial benefits from marriage: living longer, healthier, wealthier, and happier lives as a result. Women especially need close relationships with a partner in order to thrive. Our ability to nurture such relationships can benefit us mentally. A fulfilling relationship must have some reciprocity, but not necessarily tit-for-tat.

I have been in many relationships over the years. But it was when I met Albert that I realized that I had never had a nurturing relationship because I had never made up my mind to work hard toward this goal. One night following a spat, I took a good look at my husband while he was asleep. For the first time I realized that I held a special feeling in my heart for someone, something I had never experienced before. I realized that this was an opportunity to achieve my dream of having someone to really feel close to and share a good life. Of course, it has not always been easy. Sometimes I've wanted to strangle him.

I learned that regarding a mate, one has to write down needs that must be met, things that will not be accepted, things open to compromise, and things to remember. Here's my list, and although it refers to a husband, I think it applies to any mate:

- You don't have to wait for the perfect "Mr. Right." Find someone who meets most of your standards and then work to make it right.
- Mutual respect must exist in a relationship.
- You do not have to like the same things, as long as each of you have the freedom to do what you like by yourself or with your friends.
- Love must be unconditional; you give love because you love that person, not because you want to be loved in return. When you love the right person unconditionally, you will eventually be loved the way you want.

- Men sometimes don't know what we are talking about. Their brains are not wired the same way as women. I learned that when I was telling Albert something that I really wanted him to do for me, emotionally. I looked in his eyes, and although I knew he really loved me and would do anything for me, he didn't seem to have a clue about what I was trying to explain to him. The saying "you cannot get blood out of a turnip" holds true in this situation.
- A man does not have to be your best friend. That is why we have girlfriends and sisters.
- The more successful you are, the more difficult this is for the man in your life. The Y chromosome demands it. Especially if you make more money than your man, you have to constantly remind him that his emotional support is what makes you successful. I read this somewhere and it has been very helpful to me: "A man with a healthy measure of self-esteem can tolerate the super-success of his significant other without feeling diminished or threatened. The wise woman knows how to keep his ego pumped up. She lets him know that his love and support have contributed to her success, and she makes him feel like an equal partner."
- You may be independent when you are at home, but when you are with friends, especially his male friends, it is okay to be the "wife."
- Regardless of how bull-headed he may act, you must have the patience to be flexible, understanding and be able to compromise.
- My Grandma and my mother used to tell me that it was easier to catch an ant with honey than with vinegar. When Albert gets into his "unavailable mode," I leave him alone for a while.
- Whenever you do something for your partner, do it because you want to and not because you expect something in return. Keeping tabs does not work, it only creates resentment.
- Acknowledge your partner and let him know how much you appreciate him. Sometimes we forget to say this. I routinely sing "Have I told you lately that I love you" just to make Albert laugh.
- Sometimes it is difficult for men to express love the way women expect. Do not waste energy expecting a man to tell you that you look nice or that he loves you. Learn to recognize when a partner is trying to tell you they love you *their own way*. "I love you" comes in many different ways and shapes. It could be something nice that he does for

one of your relatives.

- If you are angry about something, do not discuss it then; wait until all feelings of anger have disappeared.

- Make your home a refuge for the one you love.

- Acknowledge that your partner is different from you. You don't need to change him. Your partner does not see the world through your eyes and, therefore, won't think, feel, or behave in the manner you feel most appropriate. If that is your expectation of your partner, you'll find that he will feel invalidated, misunderstood, and eventually not cared for. If you have a great need to control others, you are demonstrating how insecure you are about yourself; you are the one who is not living up to your own expectations and, therefore, finding your own life out of control.

- Take what you have learned about nurturing yourself and apply it to your partner to see what works for him. Each of us is different and requires different amounts and types of nurturing. Take the time to discover what your partner needs. You'll be very glad you did.

- Learn to appreciate the unique traits and differences in your partner. Ultimately, the recognition of differences among people allows us to release ourselves from the need to be judgmental.

- Learn the rudiments of supportive, direct, and honest communication. True and effective communication has the intent of sharing our most intimate thoughts, feelings, and perceptions. Reciprocally, we share our partner's thoughts, feelings, and perceptions.

- Know that the television remote has been surgically attached to his right hand, and that removal would require major surgery you are unable to perform. If you really need a hug while he is watching television, you will have to make do with one arm. If he is a sports fan, do not try to have important conversations during a game, unless it is a life-threatening emergency. From August through January, you should not expect him to leave the house on Monday night, Sunday afternoon, whenever play-offs are approaching, or during a major game. To make life easier, add sports words to your vocabulary.

Run From Violent Relationships

"It is better to be alone than in bad company."
—author unknown

The only situation without compromise is a violent relationship. Each year, almost 2 million women are abused by their spouses. Abuse can include, but is not limited to, beating, emotional humiliation, and rape. The majority of female homicide victims are killed by abusive partners. Abuse occurs in all walks of life, regardless of wealth, education, ethnicity or religion. In order to stop the violence, the woman must leave. But women often stay because of physical, financial and psychological dependency. Often, the children are also being abused. If a woman takes her children with her when she leaves, she may not earn enough money to afford childcare. Finally, battering can change a woman psychologically, making her believe the abuse is her own fault since she's "no good" as a wife and/or mother.

Any type of forced sex – even by a date, friend or spouse – is rape. Unfortunately, more women than ever before continue to live in fear of their rapists. The rape victim continues to be blamed for the crime, and only about 7% of all rapes are ever reported to authorities.

If you find yourself in this situation, you can take control! You may feel humiliated, isolated, and afraid to be examined medically. You are not alone. Counseling and support groups (low-cost or free) are available everywhere and can help you find the strength to realize that you are not to blame, and bring the batterer into the criminal justice system.

Rape is now considered a war crime.

You can call the National Council on Child Abuse and Family Violence from anywhere in the United States at 1-800-222-2000. A great book that you should read is *What Did I Do to Deserve This* by Dr. Joan McNeill. Information about marriage education skills can be found on the Internet at http://www.smartmarriages.com.

RELATIONSHIP WITH YOUR CHILDREN

I may not have given birth myself – I was always too chicken – but I am a mother in many ways. Every year I receive cards on Mother's Day. I am the first-born of six children, and as such, had to help my mother raise my two youngest siblings, Massou and Jacky. I call Jacky my brother/son and he tells me that I am the best mother/sister.

I have helped deliver more than 1,500 babies, and counseled and consoled many new mothers. I am always there for my siblings and my many nieces and nephews. I am "Tattie," auntie, or Tante Carolle, to the many children of my friends. For many years I served as a mentor to children of all ages, to college students at San Diego State University, and to post-graduate and medical students at the University of California San Diego. That I am someone who cares allows me to have an impact on these children, even though I merely repeat what their parents have told them all along.

Unfortunately, parents are not required to be licensed prior to having children and raising a child becomes, largely, a matter of trial and error. Children are innocent beings, utterly defenseless when brought into this world. Unfortunately, some children find themselves being abused mentally, physically, and sexually, and not being rescued by the adults who are supposed to protect them. Some abusers who abuse children mentally or emotionally may actually believe they are doing so for the child's own good. If you have children, or plan to have children, here are some thoughts to ponder:

* By age 8 a child's self-esteem, how he/she is going to see him/herself, has already been sealed.

* Always remember that you are setting examples for those around you. Children don't "Do as I say," they "do what they see." So, if you tell white lies, cheat on your taxes, or get free cable, you are teaching your children to be dishonest. If you smoke, don't be surprised when they experiment with drugs or alcohol. If you are racist or prejudiced, they will grow up just like you. According to a national survey, conducted September 14 through 16, 2001, and published in *The New England Journal of Medicine*, parents who experienced major symptoms of stress were more likely to report that their children were also

having trouble. According to Earlene Dunbar, the head elementary school counselor for the San Diego Unified District, when it comes to tragic situations, the biggest impact on children is how their parents handled the situation.

- Just because you were raised poor and fought to improve your own situation does not mean your children should "suffer like you did." The goal should be to teach your children the values you developed during the hard times.

- Never be too busy working that there is no time to spend with your children. Material things are a poor substitute for your love and attention.

- Children who have been abused may end up in abusive relationships as an attempt to heal their relationship with their abusers, or they, themselves, may become an abusive parent or spouse.

- When parents continually criticize a child, or they are emotionally absent, or act as though nothing the child does is good enough, the child strives endlessly to please the parent. As adults, they may choose partners who remind them of that parent in an attempt to heal themselves.

- Do not be over-critical of your children. It is true that you want the best out of them, but do not crush their sense of who they are, or make their accomplishments seem worthless.

- Children need to be hugged. Often. And to be told that you love them.

- Accept your children for who they are and love them *unconditionally*.

- Learn to delegate responsibilities appropriately. Expect your children to help more as they grow older. In the process, teach them about responsibility.

- Children are not leaving the nest as young as they once did. The cost of providing for oneself has drastically increased over the past several decades. This does not mean that you have to *mother* them for the rest of your life. This postpones your child from learning responsibility. At some point, the umbilical cord has to be cut.

RELATIONSHIP WITH YOUR FAMILY

Women naturally need close relationships with family members, friends, or a partner, in order to thrive. Research has demonstrated that a woman's ability to nurture relationships can benefit her both mentally and physically. Relationships are essential to a woman's well-being in every stage of her life. Traditionally, women have been raised to be companions, mothers, spouses, and caretakers for the sick and for elderly parents. I've found that self-reflection about the type and depth of personal relationships and friendships are especially crucial during midlife and menopause.

Women who maintain close ties to their families are less likely to be sick than those who keep to themselves. Unfortunately, a majority of women have conflicts with family members. I see many women in my medical practice who are stressed due to relationship conflicts.

More people need to realize that just because someone is your relative, you do not have to be friends with them. Mutual respect is the basis of any good relationship. If it does not exist, one has to find the courage – which is very, very difficult to do – to repair or end the relationship.

Today I have good relationships with my relatives and siblings. However, it took time, forgiveness, and acceptance to accomplish this. Once, when I was complaining about my sister to my therapist, she commented that, while my sister was indeed my sister, she did not have to be my friend. This was one of the most liberating comments I ever heard.

I was so empowered by that comment that I decided that I was not going to put up with my sister any longer. I did not want to waste my money calling her in South America, so I called my mother and asked her to tell my sister, the next time she called, that I thought she was a witch. My sister and I did not speak for a long time. But relationships can very well change over time. Now, after many years and many discussions, my sister and I are best friends.

After Grandma died, my aunt "Tatante" came to live with me in 1993. She was the same old witch. In her eyes, I could never do anything right. No matter that I had become a successful doctor, I was still that four year-old girl that she could hurt again and again. Once, I con-

fronted my aunt, but she started to cry, said she had done so much for me and that I was a persona ingrata. She was old, with no children of her own to care for her, so it was my duty to take care of her.

After two years of living with Tatante and dealing with the changing state of managed care, I ended up in my own mid-life crisis. My sister Marise came to the rescue and took Tatante to live with her in Miami. The decision for Tatante to move to Miami did not come easily. The idea made me sick and I was plagued with guilt. How could I not want her to live with me when she raised me when my mother could not? She had no children of her own. How could I abandon her?

It is hard to find the courage to tell a family member they are poisonous to our whole being. I have also found that the more negative the relationship, the more difficult it is to end. For this reason, many people prefer not to rock the boat and remain in these abusive relationships. Making the decision to leave is sometimes worse than staying put.

One way or another we have to find the courage to confront family members who continue to poison us. This can be through forgiveness or by limiting their contact and influence. I often tell friends and patients not to talk with poisonous people if they don't have to. This is why we have caller ID, answering machines and voice mail.

The Stress of Caregiving

One of the most common stressors that confront women is caring for those they love. They care for their children, their spouses, their parents, and their spouse's parents. Many women are already dealing with the challenges of mental or physical disability, or prolonged illness. For other women, these challenges may be lurking just around the corner.

Dealing with the long-term care needs of an aging parent is often an emotionally and financially significant life event. One survey revealed that about 50% of Alzheimer caregivers report they suffer from depression, and 80% say they frequently experience high levels of stress.

A stressful burden is placed on family members when an elderly parent is in need of long-term care, has no long-term care insurance, and has insufficient income from social security to provide for these needs. Much of our elderly population depends on social security payments averaging $750 a month; a decent assisted-living facility costs at least $3,000 a month. Only after an elderly person has spent down their entire life savings for their care needs, can they qualify for assistance from most state agencies.

After my mother's first stroke, she required 24-hour care until her death 14 months later. At the time she was receiving $500 a month. She had no savings and, like many of our elderly, no long-term care insurance. She could have qualified for assistance but because of our Haitian culture, we never considered placing her in a facility to receive care. Our parents took care of us as children, and expected us to care of them when they grew older. My mother's illness became a financial and emotional dilemma. It was difficult watching her deteriorate. The financial burden was tremendous.

I have many patients who complain of stress-related disorders that are the result of the emotional and financial stress of caring for an elderly relative. On the day my mother died, I was in a public restroom and heard the voice of an exasperated mother speaking to her young child. The mother was complaining about the child wetting her pants just a few minutes after she asked if she needed to go the toilet before leaving home. She was so angry that I was afraid she would hit the child. As I left the stall, I saw a young woman screaming at an elderly woman. I could see the desperation in the eyes of the younger woman, who was in tears. I knew how hard it was for me to care for my mother. I ran toward her, caught her in my arms, and cried.

I learned that her name was Monica, and she had two small children of her own. She was the only one available to care for her mother, who had been diagnosed with dementia six months earlier. Monica was mentally and physically exhausted. She felt guilty asking anyone for help because her mother had cared for her as a child, and she felt she was obligated to reciprocate. I encouraged her to put aside her "guilt" and ask for help.

Studies have demonstrated that most caregivers do not know how to ask for help. Caregivers should be aware of the signs that indicate they are stressed and need help. Some of these signs are: anger, anxiety, denial, depression, exhaustion, health problems, irritability, lack of concentration, sleeplessness, and social withdrawal.

The challenge is to provide the best possible long-term care without placing financial and emotional hardship on the rest of the family. Having a plan for your long term care needs, as well as for those of a loved one, can help to ease some of the stress. (See "long-term care insurance" in the financial section of this book.) Caregivers can also contact local assistance organizations, such as the Alzheimer's Society, to learn what resources may be available.

RELATIONSHIP WITH FRIENDS

Women who have a network of friends with whom they socialize regularly are less likely to be sick or depressed compared with women who keep to themselves. I feel that I am especially lucky to have a network of friends that I can count on.

I did not know how important friendship was until I received a telephone call from my friend, Nicole. Her first-born son, Phillip, also my godson, was leaving for college. She called me to tell me that she hopes that Phillip will find a good friend at school, the kind of friend she felt I had been for her. We both started to cry.

That night I realized how important Nicole had been to me. She was also from Haiti. She and I met in New York, lived together during medical school, and traveled to Jamaica together for an internship. We were both penniless, but shared the same vision of becoming a doctor, regardless of what it took. We supported each other through thick and thin, always looking after each other. Having her in my life made the tough times easier. Nicole taught me that it is okay to disagree and remain good friends. Once, after having had a loud argument, I contemplated moving out. A few hours later, I heard a knock on my door. I refused to answer. She kept knocking until I finally let her in. "What are you doing? How come you are not ready?" she asked. We had planned to see a movie that afternoon. I was upset. How could I go to a movie with her? She explained that our fight had nothing to do with our plans, and we could continue our fight after the movie. I reluctantly went with her. The movie was one of those tearjerkers. We had money for only one bag of popcorn. We dried our tears with one hand, and guarded our share of the popcorn with the other. By the end of the movie we were friends again. Nicole became a lifetime friend.

Each friend can support you in a different aspect of your life. Perhaps for a lifetime, or for only a time.

Being a woman, it can be difficult to understand a man's thoughts and behaviors. Having friends of both sexes to help sort things out can be invaluable.

Here is what I have learned about friendships:

- A friend is someone you can call anytime, day or night, and know that the person will be there.
- Real friends are there to support us, as well as our dreams.
- Never lend money to a friend. This is a sure way to end a friendship.
- Friendship is give and take.
- Friendship takes time to nurture.
- Take time to let your friends know how important they are to you.
- Friends come into our lives for a reason, a season, or for a lifetime. Sometimes we grow apart and need to know the time has come to go our separate ways.

RELATIONSHIP WITH YOUR COMMUNITY

Studies show that social ties boost the immune system and improve overall health. It is good to be part of a community, such as your church, social service agencies, community theatres, clubs or associations. Close-knit communities tend to experience a lower incidence of heart attack and suicide. Since the September 2001 terrorist attacks, we have begun to strengthen our community ties, but there is still much that we must accomplish. Americans are often too busy to meet next-door neighbors, let alone seek to become involved in their lives.

Community is not just our immediate surroundings or neighborhoods; it encompasses cities, states, our country and the world. We are each a citizen of the world; we do not live in a vacuum. What we do affects each and every one of us.

"Each of us has something unique to give. Sometimes, we can make a big difference just by saying a kind word, smiling, giving an advice or just being at someone's side when in need. The world is both around us and within us. It will be transformed by our efforts, courage, and our love. Each one of us has something unique to bring to the others and so many people are hoping for a word, a smile, and advice, a visit even a silent one. The world is together in us and around us and changes with the effort of each one of us, from our strength, from our love."

—author unknown

Be a Volunteer

Volunteering and mentoring help make us better citizens while helping those in need. Whenever I hear anyone complain about being unhappy, I suggest they volunteer for a cause, or to become a mentor. When we volunteer it provides us with the opportunity to give back to our communities. In my case, volunteering for charity saves me from taking myself too seriously…

The previous owner of my home had two cats. Unfortunately, I am terribly allergic to animals with fur. I was told that a good cleaning would be sufficient, so I bought the house. The first night in my home I ended up sleeping on a sofa in an uncarpeted room instead of my comfortable bed. I could not breathe in any room with carpet. I had the carpet removed the very next morning. My new carpet could not be installed for 10 days. I cursed every time I stepped onto the cold cement floor.

While working as a volunteer at the Rachel Center during those 10 long days, I met Betty. Betty was about my age, had previously had a home, a husband, and a job. She lost her husband due to severe illness, then her job, and, finally, her home. Betty had been homeless for six months. She occasionally slept out in Balboa Park, and had been raped once.

Meeting Betty was a wake-up call for me. Sometimes, we forget how lucky we are until there is a comparison. Later that night, instead of cursing the cold cement, I thanked God for all that I had.

I feel blessed to have been able to get a good education, become a physician, live in America, and then return to Haiti to give back to my people. Volunteering keeps me grounded.

So be a volunteer. Volunteer *your time* for a cause you admire, and you may reap more benefits that you ever expected. Sure, donate money when you can, but remember that the highest level of charity is to make someone self-sufficient so that they don't need to take charity.

Be a Mentor and Role Model

Sharing life experiences, skills, and personal perspectives with others who want to learn can be very rewarding. I have always taken the time to mentor young students here in America. I gave free lectures at elementary schools, junior high schools, high schools, and universities. Through the years, many students, of all races and social backgrounds, who have aspired to enter the health-care field, have spent time in my office, and time doing rounds with me at the hospital.

My niece, Judive, always said she wanted to be a doctor just like Auntie Carolle. It was not an easy road for her, but after a long struggle, she graduated from the University of Ohio in 2000. According to custom, graduates choose the doctor who was most influential in their life, to walk to the podium with them to receive their diploma. Having had no children of my own, I always tried my best to influence young people around me. Being with Judive throughout the ceremony, and walking with her while the whole family looked on, proved that it worked.

Each of us has something good to give, and when we share our time, it can only make this world a better place.

Be a Responsible Citizen

As a citizen of Planet Earth, I believe:

- We should not stand by and accept the inequities we see before us. We should make sure that every human being, regardless of his or her skin color, gender, ethnicity, creed, and physical ability, should share the same opportunities.
- Intolerance should not be part of our vocabulary.
- It is our duty to vote; there is too much apathy towards our government. We need to be part of the electoral process.
- We should do our best not to abuse this earth, and strive to make it a better place than before we were here.

The time is right for *women* to step up to leadership roles in their neighborhoods, communities, countries, and around the world. I take this responsibility seriously.

During frequent visits to Haiti, we have accomplished much. We believe that the overall health of a village does not exist solely due to provision of medical care. It is important to provide vocational training so that children living in poverty may have some hope for the future. As Haiti's unemployment rate is nearly 95%, enrichment programs are vitally important.

A lot was accomplished during my summer visit in June 2001. Two of role model Professor Aubies' dreams were realized. I raised enough money to buy land for a playground, the first in the southeastern part of Haiti. And, through a small grant from the Notes of Hope Foundation, 6 second-hand musical instruments were purchased in the Dominican Republic for his dream of teaching music. On the day of the inauguration I learned that these poor families hired a part-time music teacher from a nearby town. The teacher borrowed four additional instruments and the children entertained us with a marching band. With tears in our eyes, we listened as the children played the national anthem of their country.

A small arts program was funded and forty children were needed to create a mural for a collaborative project, The Art Miles.

Instead of forty, eighty shy but eager children from the village showed up, some of them having walked miles from homes without electricity or running water, on empty stomachs. These children, ranging in age from 5 to 20 years old, had never seen television, had never held a paintbrush, and had never done a collective project before!

First we fed them. Following some simple instructions, the children produced a magnificent 12 x 5 foot mural on canvas with acrylic paints, and the most creative, colorful, individual paintings on Bristol paper. People who have seen the efforts of these children have been moved to tears. With great care and attention to detail, they painted what they saw around them. The results are astonishing-colorful, accurate depictions of their village lives-and many show real artistic talent. They were so proud.

While learning how to express themselves and use their creativity, these young Haitian children also learned about discipline, sharing, and working together. This positive experience affected not only the children, but spread to their families and throughout their villages.

During one break, a young lady named Anite approached me. "Moin rinmin' Dr. Carolle. Moin rinmin' ampil." "I love you Dr. Carolle. I love you a lot." I was touched to see the expression of love in her eyes. Maybe she was 15 or 16. It is difficult to guess many of the children's ages as malnutrition causes them to look younger. I was also surprised to hear a teenager express love for an adult so freely. "Why do you love me so much?" I asked her. "Because of the way you are and the way you made us feel," was her reply. She asked for a picture of me to look at when she is sad, because it would make her feel better.

On Tuesday, September 11, my husband Albert and I we were saddened and shocked by the terrorist attacks. I could not stop crying. Every time I heard about or saw the devastation caused by the planes crashing into the Trade Center towers, I heard the loud and painful crash in my head. I found myself wrenched back to Haiti, when I had heard a similar explosion, "BOOM!" My girlfriend and I hid in a shop. No one knew what had happened. We had no telephone or radio. For the next two hours, which seemed like an eternity, the explosions continued. We could smell the smoke in the air. We all thought we were going to die. But we survived. Papa Doc had sent his *tontons macoutes* to arrest General Cayard, the head of the Navy. Instead of surrendering, he took refuge on one of the battleships and bombed the palace. The explosions were from canons firing over our heads.

My mind could find no comfort on September 11. And then the mail arrived. I found a letter from an unknown sender, mailed from New York. Inside was a letter from Anite in Haiti. Whenever I received a letter from any of the children of La Vallee, it was invariably a request for money to pay for school stuff, or requests for tapes for them to learn English, French-English dictionaries, or solar scientific calculators. This letter was different.

> *Dear Dr. Carolle:*
>
> *It is with immense pleasure that I take the time to write you this letter. How are you? Thanks to God, I am okay.*
>
> *The reason I am writing is to say hello and to tell you that I think of you often. I wish that you did not live so far apart so I could see you more often. Dr. Carolle, I love you. Don't ever forget that I love you with all my heart. You are forever engraved in my memory. When I think of you when I am sad, I just have to look at your smiling picture and I just start to smile. I have found a friend in you.*
>
> *I pray everyday that God guides your steps, protects you, and makes all your dreams come true. Be happy, and have a nice vacation.*
>
> *Your friend who loves you, Anite*

I cried reading her letter, and was sobbing at the end. What a beautiful gift received at a perfect time. Anite could not afford to buy stamps. She wrote the letter on August 20, gave it to someone who was traveling to New York, who then mailed it to me.

That comforting letter on September 11 confirmed all I believed, that taking time to love, accept and be tolerant of all, can only make this world a better place. Some people from other parts of the world plotted to hurt Americans that day. Somewhere else, a girl that I had empowered took the time to write words that balanced the universe.

🏼

CONCLUDING THOUGHTS ON MENTAL HEALTH

Your mind can be your most powerful asset. The way you think determines the types of relationships you have. Much of your reality, and therefore the quality of your life, is created by your mind. If you think you can do something, you can. If you think you can't, you can't! Some say you are what you eat – but I believe that you are what you *think*.

Here are some tips on keeping your mind healthy and positive:

- Nurture all your important relationships, especially with yourself.
- Work at something you love.
- Take control of your time.
- Control stress.
- Exercise your mind by sharpening your skills at work and at play.
- Have positive role models.
- Give of yourself, share your gifts.
- Rest, get enough sleep, and time alone.
- Smile – research shows that it automatically improves mood.
- Keep perspective. As author John Andrew Holmes said, *"It is well to remember that the entire population of the universe, with one trifling exception, is composed of others."*
- Consider your thinking as if it were a product, and check its quality control.
- Fuel your mind with love and passion for life.

Resources

Always Change a Losing Game, Playing At Life To Be The Best You Can Be, David Posen, MD
Staying Afloat When the Water Gets Rough, How To Live In A Rapidly Changing World, David Posen, MD
Get a Live Without Sacrificing Your Career, Dianna Booher
Men Are from Mars, Women Are from Venus, John Gray Ph.D.
Men, Women and Relationships, John Gray Ph.D.

Getting Back Together: How to Create a New, Loving Relationship with Your Old Partner and Make it Last! by Bettie Youngs Bilicki, Ph.D. and Masa Goetz, Ph.D.
To receive this book, send $15.00 to:
Masa Goetz, Ph.D.
1319 Missouri St.,
San Diego, CA 92109

Section Two

BODY

YOUR
PHYSICAL
HEALTH

Your Physical Health

How you take care of your body determines the quality of your life. Physical health has to do with the body you were born with *and* how you treat it throughout your life. Anything less than a healthy physical body presents a significant challenge to your spirit in carrying out your life's work.

You can guard and improve your health by being pro-active. Studies repeatedly show that the risk of the most prevalent diseases and the leading causes of death in the US (cardiovascular disease and cancer) for both men and women are related to **lifestyle** – the choices you make that affect your physical body. There are several schools of thought on how physical health can best be achieved and maintained, but they all emphasize that knowledge, diet, exercise, and rest are essential.

Knowledge involves self-awareness, prevention and professional diagnosis. When an illness is diagnosed early, treatment has the greatest potential for resulting in a cure. The majority of diseases, including cancer, can be successfully treated if discovered early.

As far as **prevention** – many studies show that modifying one's lifestyle, including proper nutrition, supplements, regular exercise, stress reduction, relaxation, prevention of sexually transmitted diseases, smoking cessation, alcohol and drug use moderation, maintaining a normal body weight, and regular checkups can reduce many of these risk factors. However, please note that disease risk is very complex and in addition to lifestyle and health choices, involves the following factors: *genetics, socioeconomic situation, culture, environment*, and *racial differences*.

This section of my book zeroes in on why and how you should be pro-active to ensure optimum health for your body – throughout your life.

🌳

YOUR ANNUAL PHYSICAL EXAM

We think alike if going to the doctor for a regular check-up is not on your list of favorite things to do. But, we *have* to do it! An annual physical exam is an excellent way to detect most health problems early rather than too late. Appropriate tests are performed according to your age. During a routine exam, your weight and blood pressure are recorded. High blood pressure has been called the silent epidemic.

> *When I was going through a lot of stress and lacked my usual energy, I reluctantly called my gynecologist (yes, doctors go to other doctors!) and scheduled my annual exam. I was shocked to find out that my blood pressure was slightly elevated. It was a wake-up call for me to do what I routinely tell my patients, "do what it takes to reduce stress."*

Your annual physical is also a good opportunity for your health-care provider to review your medical history and that of your relatives. Be prepared when you visit your doctor. Knowing your family's health history and present health status helps your health-care provider diagnose, prevent, and treat diseases. A routine urinalysis, for example, can reveal a silent bladder infection as well as diabetes that may run in your family. Because risk of disease will change as you and your relatives age, you should periodically reevaluate your entire family's health.

Although I believe in spending quantity as well as quality time with my patients, most doctors, especially under managed care or insurance plans, are pressed for time. Maximize your visit with any health-care provider by having a list of concerns, symptoms and/or questions. Feel comfortable enough to discuss anything related to your body and your health, and realize that you have the right to be fully informed about the status of your health. Ask questions about any tests and medications prescribed. In addition to your own research, an annual checkup is also a good opportunity to discuss new prevention modalities and treatments.

As much as I hate to admit it, *doctors are not gods*! You must empower yourself with information about your physical condition and your options in order to share in the decisions that affect your health and quality of life.

🌱🌱🌱

YOUR NUTRITION AND DIET

What you eat plays an important role in maintaining good health – *Yes, you are what you eat!* What you put in your mouth determines how your body functions and how you feel. And more than that, how healthy you stay and for how long throughout your life. Your immune system, which helps your body fight infection, requires the nutrients found in a healthy, balanced diet.

Think of your body as the vehicle for your soul. It needs to be properly maintained – besides a tune-up (that dreaded physical exam) you need the right kind of gas, oil, lube and water level to run properly, otherwise you will break down on the freeway of your life! It's amazing that some of my patients eat any old junk food yet are very picky about maintaining their cars – they change their oil on schedule and buy premium gas when their car would do fine with regular unleaded.

Let's consider what you eat as the "fuel" you put in your body. Do you realize that your eating habits can be affected by your culture, religion, taste, income, family situations, mental problems, medical problems, disability, and medication? Add the enormous and often conflicting amounts of nutritional information available today and we have quite a dilemma about what we should eat and drink.

So What *is* a Healthy Diet?

A healthy diet:

- Is full of *fresh, natural foods*. Lots of vegetables and fruit. Eaten in a quiet, peaceful environment. (I know that's not easy!) *Please* read the labels on prepared foods, and be as aware as possible about what you're getting in a restaurant, especially if it's "fast food."

- Is low in *saturated fats*. If you are an American, you probably eat too much fat. Total amount of fat should be no more than 20 to 30% of the total amount of calories consumed. Saturated fats are primarily found in animal products that are also rich in cholesterol – and foods with tropical oils such as palm and coconut oils. Some studies have revealed a link between saturated fat and heart disease. There is also a link between saturated fat and a higher risk of breast cancer.

- Is low in trans-fatty acids, which are found in commercially baked goods, and foods fried with hardened vegetable oil.

- Has most of your fat from monosaturated fats, polyunsaturated fats and fish oils:

  - *Monosaturated fats* are found in olive and canola oil, and are considered healthier because of their ability to lower LDL, the "bad" cholesterol, while maintaining or raising HDL the "good" cholesterol. People who eat a Mediterranean diet, which mainly consists of monosaturated fat especially olive oil, have a lower incidence of heart disease and cancer.

  - *Polyunsaturated fats* are found in safflower, sunflower, and corn oils, and they contain omega-6 and omega-3 essential fatty acids. In places where they are consumed, there is a decrease in the risk of heart disease and the incidence of arthritis, stroke, and some types of cancer.

  - *Fish oil* contains omega-3 fatty acids, eichosapentaenoic acid (EPA), and docosahexaenoic acid (DHA). These acids have beneficial effects on many body functions, which include reducing high lipids, blood pressure, and preventing blood clots.

- Contains moderate amounts of protein (meat, fish, eggs, nuts, seeds, grain and bean combinations, and tofu). Proteins are an essential part of the structure of every living cell and are responsible for physical development and growth. Try to eat two servings of protein rich foods daily.

- Contains carbohydrates, our best source of energy. Each day, eat several servings of bread, cereal, rice or pasta, fruit, and vegetables. But be careful – a "serving" is not large – it does not mean a bowl full – it means approximately what fits in your palm!

- Is low in salt. Use herbs and seasonings instead.

- Is low in cholesterol. Cholesterol is a type of fat found in animal-derived food sources, including meat, eggs and dairy products. The human body also synthesizes cholesterol as the first step towards producing various hormones and enzymes. When cholesterol in the bloodstream is high, it sticks to the inside walls of the blood vessels, making them narrower and sometimes blocking them entirely. Cholesterol settles in the coronary arteries, endangering the heart. When it builds up in the arteries of the neck, it increases the chance of stroke, endangering the brain. Be careful, certain foods may be cholesterol free but are high in fat, like nuts.

- Is rich in fiber. Some fiber is not digestible in our diet and provides bulk that helps our digestive system break down and assimilate food smoothly. It can also help you lower your cholesterol. Fiber can be found in complex carbohydrates like cereals, wheat flour, rice, corn, pasta, beans and vegetables. Many patients who come to see me complaining of constipation get relief when they add fiber to their diet. Useful fiber additions to the diet include flax seed and psyllium.

- Should include drinking six to eight, eight-ounce glasses of liquid a day. Plain water is the best, but not out of the tap in all areas. Water helps ward off constipation and keeps internal organs like the liver and kidneys functioning properly.

- Has as few *preservatives, artificial food colorings, refined flour and sugar* as humanly possible.

Eating a balanced diet can help you:
- Keep your energy level *up*
- Maintain a healthy weight
- Lower your risk of certain types of cancer, heart disease, strokes, and diabetes
- Manage high blood pressure, diabetes and high cholesterol
- Prevent constipation

I believe that you can eat almost anything in *moderation* unless you have a medical problem. If you eat something and notice that you have a lack of concentration, or experience joint pain or digestive troubles, it is a sign to reevaluate that food.

What About Vitamins and Supplements?

About 6 out of 10 Americans take vitamins and dietary supplements: They spend an amazing amount of money hoping it will keep them young and prevent disease. Vitamins are organic compounds needed in small amounts for body functioning that cannot be manufactured by the body itself.

The US Food and Nutrition Board of National Academy of Sciences set the values for the Recommended Dietary Allowance (RDA) based on human and animal research. They usually meet every five years to review current research on nutrients.

The RDA is set at the minimum amount needed to prevent scurvy, pellegra and other severe deficiency diseases, however it is not a gauge of *optimum levels* needed or required by some people to function at even reasonable levels of performance. Please educate yourself carefully on this topic.

A Recommended Dietary Allowance is established for protein, vitamin A, D, E, K and B-6, B-12, C, thiamin, riboflavin, niacin, folate, calcium, phosphorus, magnesium, iron, zinc, iodine and selenium. The recommended amount is set to cover 98% of all normal healthy persons in the United States. *It does not cover the nutritional needs of people with illness or chronic disease.*

Congress defined the term "dietary supplement" in the Dietary Supplement Health and Education Act (DSHEA) as a product taken by mouth that contains a "dietary ingredient" intended to supplement the diet. The dietary ingredients in these products may include: vitamins, minerals, herbs or other botanicals, amino acids, and substances such as enzymes, organ tissues, glandulars, and metabolites. Dietary supplements can also be extracts or concentrates, and may be found in many forms such as tablets, capsules, softgels, gelcaps, liquids, or powders. They can also be in other forms, such as a bar, but if they are, information on their label must not represent the product as a conventional food or a sole item of a meal or diet. Whatever their form may be, DSHEA places dietary supplements in a special category under the general umbrella of "foods," not drugs, and requires that every supplement be labeled a dietary supplement.

My general advice is to try to get your vitamins from eating a healthy diet. But many of us don't *do* that, plus we live in such a polluted environment that our bodies have not evolved to cope with the extra toxic debris we are confronted with on a daily basis. Use of *proper supplementation for your body* can help compensate for this and improve overall well being.

Who Should Supplement?

(Source: The Council for Responsible Nutrition)

• People who have intestinal conditions such as chronic pancreatis, irritable bowel syndrome and inflammatory bowel disease, which can cause problems with absorption of the nutrients you eat.

• Those of you on diets that eliminate key nutrients or provide less than 1,200 calories per day.

• Cancer patients with little appetite and poor nutrition.

• Strict vegetarians need extra protein, vitamin B12, D and calcium.

• Menstruating women need extra iron.

• Midlife and postmenopausal women need extra calcium.

• Women of childbearing age, pregnant women, and those who are breast-feeding do benefit from a prenatal vitamin. Prenatal vitamins contain folic acid that cannot be obtained with a regular diet and that has been proven to prevent a birth defect called a neural tube defect.

General Guide To Maximum Vitamin Dosages per Day

Vitamin A .... 3,000 — 5,000 IU

Vitamin B-1 .... 1.0 mg, additional 0.4 mg suggested for pregnant women

Vitamin B-2 .... 1.7 mg, additional 0.3 mg suggested for pregnant/ lactating women

Vitamin B-6 .... 3 mg

Vitamin B-12 ..... 4 mcg

Vitamin C............ 500 mg.

Vitamin D .... 400 IU

Vitamin E .... 400 IU.

Folic Acid........... 400 — 1000 mcg

Selenium .... 55 — 200 mcg

Zinc .... 15 — 30 mg

Iron .... 18 mg, additional 10 mg suggested for pregnant/ lactating women

Potassium .... 1,500 — 2,000 mg

Magnesium .... 300 mg

Calcium .... 1,000 — 1,500 mg

Vitamin A   Also called beta-carotene or Retinol. Fat Soluble.

Functions

Vision, reproduction, growth, tissue repair, bone formation, hormone synthesis, antioxidant (in beta-carotene form).

Deficiencies

Night blindness, impaired bone growth, susceptibility to infection, rough skin.

Food Sources

Fortified foods (mostly dairy), liver, eggs, green leafy vegetables, oranges and red fruits and vegetables.

Vitamin B-1   Also called Thiamine. Water Soluble

> *Functions*
>
>> Supports appetite, supports nervous system function, participates in enzymatic energy release of carbohydrates.
>
> *Deficiencies*
>
>> Beriberi, heart irregularity, edema, mental confusion, central nervous system complications, muscle weakness, impaired growth.
>
> *Toxicity*
>
>> Rare. Rapid pulse, weakness, headaches, insomnia, irritability.
>
> *Food Sources*
>
>> Beef, pork, liver, legumes, fish, poultry, yeast, wholegrain breads, pasta, nuts.

Vitamin B-2   Also called Riboflavin. Water Soluble

> *Functions*
>
>> Participates in enzymatic energy release of carbohydrate, fat and protein, promotes vision and skin health.
>
> *Deficiencies*
>
>> Eye problems, weakness, sore throat, skin disorders.
>
> *Toxicity*
>
>> None known. Possible interference of other B vitamins.
>
> *Food Sources*
>
>> Milk / dairy, dark green vegetables, eggs, yogurt, enriched breads/cereals, liver, meat.

Vitamin B-6   Also called Pyrodoxine or Pyridoxal. Water Soluble.

> *Functions*
>
>> Fat and protein metabolism, antibody formation, red blood cell formation, involved in converting tryptophan to niacin, necessary for the conversion of homocysteine to cystathionine. It also inhibits platelet aggrega-

tion that occurs in atherosclerosis.

Deficiencies

Central nervous system disorders, seizures, dermati tis, angular

stomatitis, anemia, muscle weakness, kidney stones.

Toxicity

Depression, fatigue. irritability, headaches, can be neu rotoxic.

Food Sources

Meats, fish, green leafy vegetables, legumes, bananas, whole grains.

Vitamin B-12 Also called Cobalamin. Water Soluble.

Functions

Red blood cell formation, nervous system maintenance.

Deficiencies

Anemia, nerve degeneration, paralysis, smooth tongue, fatigue, dementia, depression. Strict vegetarians should consult a physician for B12 supplements.

Toxicity

None known.

Food Sources

Found almost exclusively in animal products. Meats, fish, poultry, milk, eggs, yeast, cheese

Vitamin C Also called Ascorbic Acid. Water Soluble.

Functions

Antioxidant, collagen synthesis, wound healing, infection resistance, iron absorption, maintains the integrity of the arterial walls, reverses oxidation, and prevents free radical formation.

Deficiencies

Anemia, scurvy, depression, infections, bleeding gums,

muscle degeneration, poor wound healing, atheroscle-
rotic plaques, capillary hemorrhaging

Toxicity

Nausea, diarrhea, red blood cell damage, nosebleeds,
abdominal cramps.

Food Sources

Citrus fruits, berries, mangos, papayas, melons,
tomatoes, potatoes, green peppers and leafy green
vegetables.

Vitamin D Fat Soluble.

Functions

Calcium and phosphorus metabolism, bone formation,
calcium absorption.

Deficiencies

Rickets in children, osteomalacia in adults, abnormal
growth, joint pain, soft bones, muscle weakness, bony
deformities, neuromuscular irritability.

Toxicity

Raised blood calcium, constipation, weight loss, irritability, weakness, nausea, kidney stones, mental retardation, physical retardation hypercalcemia,
hypercalciuria, soft tissue calcifications.

Food Sources

Fortified milk/dairy, fish, liver, eggs.

Non-Food Source

Sunlight (at least 15 minutes a day)

Vitamin E* Also called Tocopherols and Tocotrienols. Fat Soluble.

Functions

Antioxidant, cellular membrane stability, red blood cell
protection.

Deficiencies

    Muscle wasting, red blood cell damage, hemolytic anemia, hemorrhaging, reproductive failure, neurological abnormalities.

Toxicity

    Rare. Possible general discomfort.

Food Sources

    Vegetable and seed oils, nuts, whole grains, wheat germ, green leafy vegetables.

    *Several studies have suggested that vitamin E may protect against heart disease, colon cancer and Parkinson disease. It has been demonstrated that vitamin E may help prevent and protect against heart disease by blocking oxidation of LDL. In two large studies, participants who took at least 100 IU per day of vitamin E supplements for more than two years, experienced a 45% reduced incidence of heart disease than those participants who did not take vitamin E. It has been revealed that vitamin E can reduce the risk of heart attack by 77%. One study, of people over age 65 who took 200 IU/day, revealed an increased antibody response against disease.

    Vitamin E can also help delay functional deterioration among patients with Alzheimer's disease, and may improve immune function, thus producing a better antibody response. Vitamin E dosages higher than 400 IU may be too much and may affect blood clotting or promote bleeding, similar to the effects of aspirin. Very large doses may interfere with vitamin D metabolism, and may weaken bones and reduce vitamin A storage in the liver.

Folic Acid*   Also called Folate. Water Soluble.

    Functions

        Red blood cell formation, new cell division, protein metabolism, essential for the metabolism of homocysteine.

    Deficiencies

        Anemia, diarrhea, smooth tongue, depression, heartburn.

Toxicity
> Insomnia, irritability, diarrhea, may mask B-12 deficiency.

Food Sources
> Green leafy vegetables, liver, legumes, seeds, and enriched breads, cereals, rice, and pasta.

*The average dietary intake of folic acid in the US is only 225 micrograms per day. There is evidence that increasing folic acid, by 600 micrograms per day minimizes the risk of neural tube defect, and possibly cardiovascular disease. The Nurses Health Study documented a decrease in morbidity and mortality with an adequate daily dietary intake of folate (400 micrograms) and vitamin B6 (3 mg).

Selenium   Trace Mineral

Functions
> Protects against oxidation.

Deficiencies
> Anemia (rare).

Toxicity
> Digestive disorders, dermatologic lesions.

Food Sources
> Seafood, meats, grains, Brazil nuts.

Zinc   Trace Mineral

Functions
> Transport of vitamin A, taste, wound healing, sperm production, fetal development. Plays a part in many enzymes, hormones (insulin), genetic material, and proteins. Helps protect the eye macula (center of the retina)

Deficiencies
> Decreased appetite growth failure in children, delayed development of sex organs, reduced immune function, poor wound healing.

Toxicity
Fever, vomiting, diarrhea, gastric distress, dizziness.

Food Sources
Beef, fish, poultry, grains, vegetables.

Iron   Trace Mineral

Functions
Hemoglobin formation in red blood cells, myoglobin formation in muscle, oxygen carrier, energy utilization.

Deficiencies
Anemia, weakness, headaches, depressed immunity, behavioral abnormalities, reduced cognitive function.

Toxicity
Infections, liver damage, possible increased cancer and heart disease risk.

Food Sources
Beef, fish, poultry, shellfish, eggs, legumes, dried fruits, fortified cereals.

Potassium   Major Mineral

Functions
Protein synthesis, fluid balance, muscle contraction, nerve transmission.

Deficiencies
Weakness, paralysis, mental confusion, possible death.

Toxicity
Muscular weakness, possible vomiting.

Food Sources
Fruit, vegetables, dairy, grains, legumes, beef.

Magnesium   Major Mineral

Functions
Bone mineralization, protein synthesis, enzymatic reactions, muscular contraction, nerve transmission.

Deficiencies

(Rare in non-disease state; prevalent in chronic alcoholism, renal dysfunction, hyperparathyroidism) Weakness, confusion, hypertension, arrhythmia, depressed pancreatic hormone secretion, growth failure, behavioral disturbances, muscle spasms.

Food Sources

Legumes, whole grain cereals, nuts, dark green vegetables, chocolate, mineral water.

Calcium*   Major Mineral

Functions

Principal skeletal mineral in bones and teeth, muscle contraction and relaxation, nerve function, intracellular regulation, extracellular enzyme cofactor, blood clotting, blood pressure.

Deficiencies

Osteoporosis, stunted childhood growth, possible hypertension, preeclampsia, and colon cancer.

Toxicity

Rare, due to excretion.

Food Sources

Dairy, fish (with bones), tofu, legumes, kale, broccoli, fortified foods.

*Your body needs calcium to make strong, dense bones and to enable the heart, muscles, and nervous system to work properly. The average American diet, even a healthy one, may not give you the amount of calcium you need. It has been estimated that the average person consumes about 650 mg of calcium per day. Youth, pregnant and post-menopausal women require a higher intake.

An adequate calcium intake is necessary in childhood and youth for normal bone growth, and will slow the rate of bone loss and reduce the risk of fractures in older adults. A diet low in calcium during youth can cause a lack of normal bone mass.

National Institutes of Health (NIH) Panel
Calcium Recommendation Per Day

Children and Young Adults:
age 1-10 : .... 800-1,200 mg
age 11-24: .... 1,200-1,500 mg

Adult Female:
age 25-50: .... 1,000 mg
age 50-65: .... 1,500 mg
postmenopausal/taking estrogen: .... 1,000 mg
pregnant or nursing: .... 1,200 -1,500 mg
age 65+: .... 1,500 mg

Optimally, your diet should be the first choice for increasing your calcium intake, such as eating leafy green vegetables and legumes, and calcium-fortified products. Your own food can be fortified by adding a tablespoon or two of nonfat dry milk to baked goods, hot beverages, or casseroles.

Dairy products such as milk, yogurt, and cheese not only contain calcium, but are also a major source of vitamin D; additionally they contain vitamins A, B-6, folate, riboflavin, magnesium, and potassium. Other foods such as broccoli, turnip greens, and canned salmon with bones are also great sources of calcium.

If you are taking thyroid medication, don't take it together with your calcium supplement because it decreases its absorption, making it less effective. And caffeine increases calcium losses in the urine.

Those of us who do not consume a calcium-rich diet, especially lactose-intolerant women who are perimenopausal and postmenopausal, should take a calcium supplement.

To find out how much calcium supplementation you need, keep track of calcium intake in your diet for one week, then divide the number by seven to determine your average daily intake. Take calcium supplements for the amount you are lacking.

Antioxidants

Many studies have shown that an adequate dietary intake of antioxidants may decrease your chance of developing coronary-artery disease, stroke and various kinds of cancer. Antioxidants are vitamins and minerals that neutralize free radicals by lending them electrons so they don't have a chance to damage your cells.

Antioxidants include vitamin A, beta carotene, vitamin E, selenium, zinc, vitamin C, lycopene, allicin, and capsaicin. These ingredients are present in most fruits , whole grains, seeds, vegetables, seafood, and dairy products., besides supplements

A warning though, if you're taking a statin drug and niacin to lower your cholesterol, high doses of antioxidants can suppress the boost in HDL ("good") cholesterol that you get from the drugs.

Phytoestrogens

There is growing evidence that phytoestrogens, or plant estrogens, can provide important health benefits for women. Phytoestrogen is a naturally-occurring plant sterol that has an effect similar to estrogen. Phytoestrogens are found in soybeans, flaxseed, legumes (dried peas and beans), red clover sprouts, and a number of fruits and vegetables. Asian women, especially the Japanese, experience a much lower incidence of hot flashes, heart disease, and osteoporotic fractures than American women because soy is a staple in their diet. According to a recent study, phytoestrogen intake of American women does not appear to protect them against breast cancer.

Be aware that just because a food says "soy," it does not mean that isoflavones are present. Some common examples are soy sauce, soybean oil, soy hot dogs, soy cheese, tofu yogurt, and soy bacon, all of which contain a small amount of soy. Some soy products, such as vegetarian or soy burgers, are made with "soy-protein concentrate," which contains almost no isoflavones. Look for products that say "soy-protein isolate" on the label, which indicates the isoflavones are largely retained.

Protein

There is no RDA for fat, cholesterol, sodium or carbohydrates. The RDA for protein is age and gender dependent. Women need at least the Recommended Daily Allowance for protein, which is 0.4 grams for every pound you weigh. That translates into 50 grams of protein a day for a 120-pound woman, or 60 grams for a 150-pound woman.

Some people will always be partial to meat, but to reduce the risk of heart disease and cancer, it makes sense to get some of your animal protein from chicken, fish, and low-fat milk, yogurt or cheese. You don't *have* to eat meat to get protein. Soy protein contains all the amino acids (protein building blocks) that meat does. Soy protein lowers blood cholesterol. A meta-analysis (a study that combines the results from many different research studies) found that soy protein lowered cholesterol by just over 9%, which translates into a 27% lower risk for heart attack. Try whole soybeans, soynuts, tempeh, tofu, or soy milk.

Amino Acids

Amino acids are 22 nitrogen-containing organic compounds that are the building blocks for making proteins and growing muscle.

Amino acids are classified as "essential" (which means the body cannot produce them and they must be obtained from a person's dietary intake) or "nonessential" (which means that a healthy body has the ability to produce some amount). "Nonessential" does not mean "unimportant."

Essential amino acids: Histidine, Isoleucine, Leucine, Lysine, Methionine, Phenylalanine, Threonine, Tryptophan, Valine.

Non-Essential amino acids: Alanine, Arginine, Asparagine, Aspartic Acid, Cysteine, Glutamic Acid, Glutamine, Glycine, Proline, Serine, Tyrosine.

🌿

DIETING

The Facts

It's no longer normal to be normal weight! In America, more than one out of two adults are overweight; one out of five adults and one out of seven children are obese. No wonder that in a recent survey, about 40% of the men and 70% of the women admitted that they were not happy with their weight. How many people do you know who are *always* on some kind of diet?

Here are a few scary facts – In 2000, a total of 38.8 million American adults met the classification of obesity, defined as having a body mass index score of 30 or more. This total figure represents an estimated 19.6 million men, 19.2 million women, and increases in obesity rates in nearly every sub-group of the US population. *This reflects a 61% increase in US obesity in only 9 years!*

Obesity is no longer just an American problem either. The WHO (World Health Organization) says that in the past seven years, the obesity rate of the world's population has shot up to 18%, as studied in 93 countries. We now live in a "toxic food environment" of changing lifestyles and changing diets that are causing an epidemic of obesity around the world. We eat out more because it's convenient and gotten cheaper, opportunities to eat, especially junk food, surround us all day long, and the size of restaurant portions is increasing. But so are the weights of the young and old alike. According to the Journal of American Dietary Association, kids aged 7 to 17 consume nearly twice as many calories when they eat at restaurants than at home. The percentage of children and adolescents who are obese has doubled in the last 20 years. From a young age, children must be taught they can leave the table without being stuffed!

Weight increase during midlife cannot be attributed solely to hormonal factors. Most likely, it is a combination of an age-related decrease in metabolic rate, an increase in food intake, and a decrease in physical activity. Around the globe, people are eating more and exercising less, creating "couch potatoes" and obesity-related diseases.

Diabetes and diseases such as anorexia nervosa – the relentless pursuit of thinness; bulimia nervosa – the binge-purge disorder; and binge eating disorder – also called compulsive eating, are on the rise in America and reaching other countries where plumpness used to be considered *healthy*. Often culture and sociability celebrates food and associates food with love. Food becomes a best friend or an escape in times of stress.

Warning signs of this becoming *unhealthy*, of course, are obesity, constipation, fatigue, and the inability to lose excess weight or keep it off if you do lose it.

There is no one "diet" to lose weight for everyone – what works for one person does not work for another. There are a million diets, diet books, gurus, pills, creams and systems. There is the cabbage soup diet. The Atkins diet, high protein, high fat and low carbohydrates. The Zone diet where 40% of calories are derived from carbohydrates, 30% from low-fat protein and 30% from fat – less than 10% of it saturated. The Dr. Bob Arnot's Revolutionary Weight Control Program, where high carbohydrates are consumed. The *Eat Right 4 Your Type* by Dr. Peter D'Adamo where what one consumes depends on your blood type. The Ornish low-fat diet, which is the opposite of Dr. Atkins. The Pritikin diet, low in calories and very low in fat, emphasizing fruits, grains and vegetables.

If you try fad or extreme diets, you will inevitably revert back to your old habits and gain the weight back, or worse. And some of those media-touted diets are dangerous because they deprive you of needed nutrients or put you on a speed-like trip (i.e.: Ephedra or Ma-Huang). Fasting and starving only lower your metabolic rate, making it harder to use up any calories you eat. And diuretic diets just temporarily make you lose water weight.

My Point of View

You know what works?

*True motivation to change your eating habits, eat less, eat better foods, and **exercise** more!*

I know that eating is one of life's greatest pleasures. Since there are many foods and many ways to build a healthy diet and lifestyle, there is lots of room for choice. The best way to lose weight is to combine a low-fat diet with regular exercise. When you diet, your metabolism slows down, Metabolism is the way our bodies use what we eat, producing energy. Each person has a different metabolism. Even people who don't eat a lot can have a problem losing weight if they don't exercise.

Healthy Eating Tips:

- Before eating, ask yourself: Am I really hungry? If you're really not, don't eat, or if it's a social meal, eat very small portions.
- Eat slowly and savor every bite, which means chewing each bite more.
- Do not buy tempting food at the store. Out of sight – hopefully, out of mind.
- Use "lite" or low-fat dairy products (e.g., milk, cheese, yogurt, or sour cream). Use in recipes and/or drink 1% or skim milk. You'll still get the nutrients and taste but not the fat.
- If you must use butter, margarine, mayonnaise, or salad dressings, use them sparingly.
- Fast food combines two of our favorite desires: things in a hurry and food. Unfortunately, it also tends to combine a lot of fat and calories. Plan meals better and avoid those drive-thru's.
- If you like to eat meat, you can reduce fat by choosing the leanest cuts such as beef round, loin, sirloin, pork loin chops, turkey, chicken, and roasts. All cuts with the name "loin" or "round" are lean. And if you cook it yourself, trim all visible fat and drain the grease.
- Fried foods are high in fat, which is why they probably taste good to us. If you *have* to fry, use oils sparingly (try olive and canola oils). Bake chicken without the skin. Substitute a potato for French fries.
- Snacks? They taste great, they're easy, and they satisfy our sweet and salt cravings. And crunchy food is fun. So – make your own snacks by packing little bags or containers of ready-to-eat vegetables or healthier store bought snack food, like pretzels. Keep them in your briefcase, office, car and home.
- Eating in a restaurant? Typical restaurant servings are often twice the size of a single serving. Ask for a half-size serving, or take half home. No "super-sizing," and leave off the cheese
- Just because something is fat free or low fat doesn't mean you can eat as much as you want. Many low-fat or nonfat foods are also high in calories. Low-fat frozen yogurt, for example, is high in sugar.

- If you love dessert, have some but share it with someone else, or have a small portion.
- If you start craving, go for a walk or get occupied with something.
- Thirst can be mistaken for hunger – have a large glass of water.
- Stay away from food that makes you overeat. *For me, it is cashew nuts, I can't stop eating those darn things when I start!*
- If you can't resist, have a small portion – and try not to feel guilty afterwards.

🌱🌱

EXERCISE/PHYSICAL ACTIVITY

If I could create a pill to ensure perfect health, it would be an exercise pill! It's tough to lose weight and keep it off. Do you belong to the "club" that buys exercise equipment, video tapes or gym memberships and never uses them? Then you're going to have to take my advice instead of a miracle pill!

The Facts

Exercising regularly is a good way to enjoy being in good physical condition; it helps control weight and lifts your spirits. Keep moving – anything counts! Regular exercise also helps build strong bones, lowers LDL and raises HDL, significantly reduces the risk of heart disease, lowers the risk of Type 2 diabetes, helps lower blood pressure, lowers the risk of breast and colon cancer, reduces stress, relieves insomnia, promotes digestion, increases energy and improves your sex life!

Physical inactivity is more common among women than men. And wouldn't you know it, men always burn more calories than women, no matter the equipment or exercise intensity! That's because muscle burns more calories than fat and pound for pound, men have more muscle. Also, it takes more calories to move a bigger person and men are usually bigger than women. More than 60% of US women do not engage in the recommended amount of physical activity, and more than 25% of US women are not active at all!

The loss of strength and stamina attributed to aging is in part caused by reduced physical activity, and inactivity increases with age. By age 75, about one in three men and one in two women engage in no physical activity. Among adults aged 65 years and older, walking and gardening or yard work are, by far, the most popular physical activities. Social support from family and friends has been consistently and positively related to regular physical activity.

The Risks

- Not exercising enough: It's been my experience that those people who do not take time to exercise usually are overworked, over-stressed, too tired, or simply never developed the habit. But the consequences are still the same: When you lead a sedentary life, you're at risk of obesity because you do not burn enough calories. You also have less energy and are at risk of atrophying your muscles – the old adage "use it or lose it" really applies here. You'll probably be relieved to know this: You don't have to exhaust yourself to burn off that stored fat. New studies indicate that *lower-intensity exercise does a very efficient job.*

- Exercising improperly: You can hurt yourself, especially if you do too much too soon or use apparatus like weights without knowing proper form. Take some time to warm up by stretching the leg, arm and upper-body muscles. When you've finished exercising, cool down the same way. Dress properly, especially if you exercise outdoors. If you feel any kind of pain, stop. Exercising should be for fun and to improve your health – not to hurt yourself. Listen to your body!

- Beware of becoming addicted to over-exercising. I know it's hard for most of us to believe, but some people can become "addicted," maybe to the endorphin high, or to the "avoidance of doing something else."

- Becoming dehydrated: Be sure to drink plenty of fluids while exercising, especially during hot weather, so you don't become dehydrated. Please do not make the common mistake of waiting until you're thirsty before taking a drink of water. Thirst is *not* an early signal of water needs; it's a warning sign that you're dehydrated and need to drink up – and fast. *By the time you feel thirsty you have already lost over 1% of your total body water.* Some subtle signs of dehydration include dry lips, dark colored urine, muscle or joint soreness, headaches, crankiness, fatigue and constipation. More serious complications caused by extreme dehydration include seizures, permanent brain damage, or even death.

By the way, in addition to *water*, milk, juice and soup count toward your daily fluid intake because of their high water content. But don't include alcohol, coffee, tea, and soft drinks that contain caffeine because caffeine has a diuretic effect. Since your body is nearly two-thirds water, it is important to stay ahead of dehydration. If you are out in hot, humid weather or exercising vigorously you need to replace 150% of the amount of water lost to keep hydrated. If you lose 1 pound of sweat during a workout (16 ounces) you need 24 ounces of fluid to rehydrate.

My Point of View

Find something you like to do for exercise, or let's face it, you won't stick to it. Find a convenient gym, or you won't go. Don't overdo it, or you'll get sore and tired and quit. And have your gear handy!

Start small, and add more time to your favorite activities as your body becomes more conditioned. *If you have serious medical conditions, or take prescription drugs, check with your physician before starting new or unusual exercise of any kind.*

Please balance aerobic exercise (fat burning) with anaerobic (strength training) exercise at least two or three times a week. Plan on 20-30 minutes or longer, according to your endurance. If you've been inactive for a long time, it's dangerous to overdo at the beginning. Start slowly and gradually increase the length of exercise time, maybe five to ten percent each week.

Shoot for a *target heart rate* that's appropriate for your age – about 120 heart beats per minute if you're in your 60's, 130 if you're in your 50's, and faster if you're younger.

Finding your Target Heart Rate

Let's say you are 45 years old. To determine your target heart rate in beats per minute:

1. Subtract your age from 220 (220 - 45 = 175).

2. Take 60% of the total from Step 1 to get your minimum heart rate in beats per minute (175 x .60 = *105*).

3. Take 75% of the total from Step 1 (175 x .75 = *131*) to get your maximum heart rate in beats per minute.

4. The resulting two figures represent what your target heart should be (*105* to *131* beats per minute) while exercising.

Choose a convenient time and set a goal. For example – "starting next week, I will walk three times a week for half an hour." Take a yoga class, play tennis, go biking with your kids, drive to the gym, walk around the golf course with your husband, or take the dog on long walks if you prefer the dog's company! It really keeps you motivated to have a walking companion, a workout partner or even a personal fitness trainer, if it suits your budget. *But you must make the time!* Being busy is not an excuse. We're *all* busy these days.

Big benefits of physical activity:
- Helps maintain the ability to live independently and reduces the risk of falling and fracturing bones.
- Reduces the risk of dying from coronary heart disease and of developing high blood pressure, colon cancer, and diabetes.
- Helps reduce blood pressure in some people with hypertension.
- Helps people with chronic, disabling conditions improve stamina and muscle strength.
- Helps maintain healthy bones, muscles, and joints.
- Helps control joint swelling and pain associated with arthritis.
- Reduces symptoms of anxiety and depression and improves mood and feelings of well-being.

I've been walking now for the past six years, maybe because of the beautiful weather in Southern California where I live and work. On Tuesdays and Thursdays, I use a treadmill for 47 minutes, but on Saturdays I walk 3.2 miles with my friend Laurie, on a trail around a beautiful lake. This is the amount of walking time that makes me feel better, helps me keep my weight in check and does not put too much stress on my knees. The hardest part is getting up early in the morning to use the treadmill. I make myself do it because I know that by the time I am halfway through, I will be feeling so-o-o good. If I can make time as a doctor, then you can too....Do you hear me???

🌱🌱🌱

BODY IMAGE

Television, magazines and newspapers depict very thin models to "represent" the ideal image of today's woman. People who think they're overweight spend billions of dollars each year at spas and "fat farms" and on drinks and drugs in an attempt to become thinner. Unfortunately, after a year, more than 90% of these people have regained the weight they lost and sometimes even more. The old joke about "yo-yo" diets is as true today as it ever was: "I don't have any trouble losing 10 pounds. I've done it dozens of times."

Many adolescents and some women suffer from an illness called *anorexia nervosa*. These women have a distorted image of their bodies. They think they are obese even if they weigh less than the adequate weight for their age and height. That is why they eat very little and exercise in an exaggerated manner. Because they cannot maintain the normal level of necessary estrogen, many anorexic women do not have a menstrual cycle.

Another disease is *bulimia*, or exaggerated appetite. In this case, the person eats large amounts of food and then forces herself to vomit in order not to gain weight. Some women have both illnesses. The combination of anorexia nervosa and bulimia can be life-endangering, and people who suffer from thesse conditions require medical and psychiatric treatment.

Some people who gain weight deny overeating. In reality, they may be eating more than they think without even knowing it. According to a report from Indiana University, their problem is caused by a multiple-personality disorder. They literally don't realize they are eating huge amounts of food. Psychological investigation revealed that one personality was pushing them to eat without the "real" self (which was trying to lose weight) being aware of it. The same scientists found other people who ate while they were asleep. When they woke up in the morning, their beds and night clothing were full of scraps from food that they couldn't remember eating at all. But these conditions are very rare.

Cosmetic Surgery

The Facts

Cosmetic or plastic surgery is very big business in the US and many other countries. People want to stay looking as young and slim and tight as possible – women want bigger breasts, smaller noses, men want more hair, no love handles, and lots of money is spent on liposuction, face lifts, nips, tucks and peels.

There were nearly 8.5 million cosmetic surgical and non-surgical procedures performed in 2001, according to the largest national survey to date by the American Society for Aesthetic Plastic Surgery. Women had over 7.4 million cosmetic procedures, 88% of the total, and men had over 1 million cosmetic procedures, 12% of the total. Here are a few more interesting statistics:

- From 1997-2001, there was a 304% increase in the number of cosmetic procedures.
- The number of cosmetic procedures performed on women increased 311% from 1997-2001 and the number of cosmetic procedures performed on men increased 256% from 1997-2001.
- There was a 48% increase in the number of cosmetic procedures between 2000-2001.
- The top 5 surgical procedures were: lipoplasty (385,000, up 118% since 1997); eyelid surgery (246,000); breast augmentation (217,000); nose reshaping (177,000); and facelift (117,000).
- The top 5 nonsurgical procedures were: BOTOX botulinum toxin

injection-BTX (1.6 million, up 2356% since 1997); chemical peel (1.4 million); collagen injection (1.1 million); microdermabrasion (915,000); and laser hair removal (855,000).

- The top 5 surgical procedures for women were lipoplasty, breast augmentation, eyelid surgery, nose reshaping and breast reduction.

- The top 5 surgical procedures for men were lipoplasty, nose reshaping, eyelid surgery, breast reduction (treatment of gynecomastia) and facelift.

- Baby Boomers age 35-50 had the most procedures – 44% of the total.

- Men and women age 51-64 had 25% of procedures; age 19-34 had 22%; age 65-and-older had 5%; and age 18-and-under had 3.5% of all cosmetic procedures.

- The most common procedures for age 18-and-under were chemical peel, laser hair removal, microdermabrasion, nose reshaping and collagen injection.

- Ethnic minorities accounted for 17% of all cosmetic procedures: Hispanics, 7%; African-Americans, 5%; Asians, 4%; and other non-Caucasians, 1%.

- Where cosmetic procedures were performed: office facility, 49%; hospital, 27%; free-standing surgicenter, 24%; and other, 1%.

My Point of View

When patients ask my opinion about cosmetic surgery, I usually say that it's their personal choice, and then I caution them to research procedures and surgeons carefully. Cosmetic surgery primarily addresses the visible signs – the symptoms, rather than the causes – of aging. The inevitable aging process can be temporarily retarded by surgical methods, but I'm more interested in preventive "wellness" techniques.

I know that self-acceptance and self-esteem can be closely aligned with body image, which is influenced by your culture's and your personal attitude about aging. Many Baby Boomers refuse to grow old, and "Age Management" seems to be a growing scientific field that may prove to be a highly influential phenomenon. Ultimately, it's about helping your patients learn to accept responsibility for their health and self-esteem. Personally, I prefer to mature naturally, with a smile on my face…

> *I stared at my naked self in the bathroom mirror when I recently turned 50, and liked what I saw: sagging breasts, a small pot-belly, bulges on both thighs, but still smooth glowing skin. I re-member back to the days when I was growing up in a culture where being plump was equated with wealth and health. How I recall being self-conscious about my tall, very skinny body dur-ing my teenage years! My little brother, Lesly, used to call me Gran' Pele, a witch character from our stories who dressed in black and flew on a broomstick.*
>
> *No longer "skinny," living in America, I've been on many diets trying to match this culture's ideal. That day in front of the mirror, I was surprised at how comfortable I felt looking at my-self. What I saw was the real me – healthy and beautiful. It's all a matter of attitude.*

BAD HABITS

Smoking

The Facts

Smoking is the single most preventable cause of illness and prema-ture death. Lung cancer has surpassed breast cancer as the leading cause of cancer deaths among US women. Since 1980, nearly 3 million women have died prematurely from smoking-related deaths. Smoking is also linked to early menopause, infertility, miscarriage, ectopic pregnancy, cervical cancer, de-pression, and osteoporosis.

Women tend to be heavier smokers, start at younger ages, and are less successful in quitting than men. In addition to cigarettes, small cigars have come into vogue with women smokers. Women now account for 39% of all smoking-related deaths, a proportion that has doubled since 1965.

Unfortunately, nicotine is very addictive. Addiction to smoke often starts in a social setting and many women continue to smoke alone. I hear this all the time from my patients: "I do it because I like it," "It relaxes me," "If I quit I will gain weight," and the best one yet, "I can quit any time." I say, "Prove it!"

The Risks

- Many studies have revealed a close relationship between smoking and an early occurrence of menopause.

- Women smokers also have a higher rate of bone loss after menopause, which increases their risk of osteoporosis.

- Cigarettes not only contain nicotine, a very addictive drug, but with each puff, a smoker's body is exposed to over 4,000 other chemicals, more than 40 of which are known to cause cancer.

- Women who smoke also have an increased risk of cervical cancers. The heavier the smoking, the greater the risk.

- Daily smoking is associated with a significantly increased risk of major depression. Light smokers who are depressed were three times as likely to increase their smoking. Major depression was about twice as likely to develop in heavy smokers, when compared with infrequent smokers. Similar relationships exist between depression and illicit drug use.

- Smoking is a major risk factor with respect to heart disease. Arteries of smokers, ex-smokers, and those exposed to secondhand smoke harden much faster than those of nonsmokers, thus increasing the risk of heart attack and stroke. Women smokers decrease their life expectancy by five to eight years.

- When a pregnant woman smokes, her growing baby is also smoking. The woman is at higher risk of having an *ectopic pregnancy* (in which the fetus is growing outside of the uterus), *spontaneous abortion* (a miscarriage), and *placental separation* (detachment of the placenta, or afterbirth, from the uterine wall) before the normal time. The child risks being born with low birth weight, a low IQ, and greater-than-normal chance of having upper respiratory infections during childhood, cancer and SIDS (sudden infant death syndrome).

- Secondhand smoke is responsible for 150,000 to 300,000 ailments in children per year. There is a 30% higher risk of lung cancer in women whose spouse is a smoker. Up to 35,000 deaths from heart attacks in the United States each year are thought to be caused by "passive" smoking.

My Point of View

If you smoke, you stink, and you will not spend much time in my house – or in my examining room! I am not alone in being allergic to the smell and chemicals. But I nag my patients because I care about them. If they smoke, they must quit. However, quitting can be hard. In my experience, a combination of willingness to quit, a smoking cessation program, nicotine-replacement products, and drugs such as Zyban will assure the best result. There are many reliable smoking-cessation programs available at local hospitals and at the YWCA. For a program near you, I urge you to call the American Lung Association at 800-LUNG-USA, or Smokenders at 800-828-4357.

Alcohol and Other Drug Abuse

The Facts

Alcoholism, and its consequences, is one of the major causes of death in women between 25 and 64 years of age. The physical effects of alcohol abuse include deterioration of brain activities, diminished mental alertness, lack of physical coordination, poor judgment and increased possibility of being involved in automobile accidents or other calamities, such as falling and fracturing a hip.

Alcohol abuse also leads to an increased incidence of high blood pressure, cirrhosis of the liver, obesity and stroke. Alcohol abuse has also been associated with osteoporosis or thinning of the bone and increased risk of breast cancer. If used during pregnancy, it can result in Fetal Alcohol Syndrome – birth defects in your baby.

Women who abuse alcohol may abuse other drugs as well. These include cocaine, heroin, marijuana and prescribed medicines. Alcoholic women also have a tendency to stay in abusive relationships and are more likely to engage in risky sexual behavior.

Women tend to be closet drinkers. Older women who abuse alcohol can be difficult to detect because they often live alone. Alcohol abuse also leads to an increased incidence of depression, high blood pressure, cirrhosis of the liver, obesity, stroke, and cancer. Alcohol consumption also increases the risk of breast cancer in women and has been associated with hip and forearm fracture in middle-aged women.

You may believe that alcohol may actually be beneficial to your health. But, how much alcohol is the right amount? When experts talk about drinking to protect the heart, they tend to agree that the limit is one drink for women and two for men per day. Remember that all drinks are not equal because different beverages contain varying amounts of alcohol. The right amount to qualify for a light drink is as follows: for wine, 5 ounces; beer, a single 12 ounce can or bottle; and hard liquor, 1.5 ounces of 80 proof. One must also remember that a drink does not mean the same for everyone because of differences in body weight, metabolism, and general health.

You probably consume too much alcohol if you can answer yes to any of these questions:

- Do you drink more than two alcoholic drinks a day?
- Do you crave a drink in the morning?
- Has anyone ever commented that you may be drinking too much?
- Do you feel that you have to have a drink at certain times of the day?
- Do you feel you need a drink to settle your nerves?
- When questioned, are you truthful about the amount you drink?
- Do you feel deprived if you do not drink?
- Do you often need a designated driver when you go to a party?

The abuse of prescription drugs can also be a significant problem. Women have less of a tendency to abuse illegal drugs than men; however, women abuse prescription drugs more often and frequently do so in combination with alcohol.

My Point of View

As a doctor, I do write prescriptions for my patients, but only when absolutely needed. I favor trying natural healing options rather than popping a pill for everything. If you are drinking too much, hopefully you are not in denial and will admit you need to seek help from AA or a private counselor or treatment center.

DISEASE PREVENTION

High Blood Pressure

The Facts

High blood pressure, which puts you at increased risk for heart disease and stroke, is estimated to affect 50 million Americans. Middle-age Americans have a 90% chance of eventually developing high blood pressure, according to a new study by JAMA (Journal of the American Medical Association).

The study, among the first to calculate the lifetime risk of developing the condition, involved mostly whites. Lifetime risks may be even higher for blacks, who are disproportionately affected by high blood pressure. The findings are based on an analysis of 1,298 men and women taking part in the continuing Framingham Heart Study, which began in 1948 and has examined participants every two years.

The authors estimated the lifetime risk of developing high blood pressure among 55-year-olds and 65-year-olds over a follow-up period of 20 to 25 years. Nearly 85% of the participants eventually developed at least mildly high blood pressure – readings of 140 over 90 or more. Between 35% to 44% developed moderate or severe high blood pressure – *160 over 100 or higher.* After taking into account those patients taking medication that lowered their blood pressure, the researchers estimated the lifetime risk of developing high blood pressure at 90%. But experts say many can still beat the odds with diet and exercise.

My Point of View

Maintaining ideal body weight and getting adequate exercise and nutrition – including avoiding too much alcohol and salt – can help prevent high blood pressure.

Heart Disease and Hypertension

The Facts

Cardiovascular disease (CVD) – affecting the heart ("cardio") and blood vessels ("vascular") – is the number one cause of death. About 370,000 women die of heart disease each year. It is also the disease most able to be controlled by your number one health provider – *YOU*.

- One out of every two women dies each year of heart disease.
- Since 1984, CVD-associated mortality for women has surpassed that for men.
- One in nine women experiences some form of CVD between the ages of 45 and 64.
- One in three women experiences some form of CVD after age 65.
- About 250,000 women die from a heart attack each year.
- If a woman has a heart attack, she is twice as likely as a man to die within the first few weeks.
- More women than men die during the first year after a heart attack.

The Risks

- Age: The older you are, the greater your risk. With age, blood vessels become narrower and less flexible.
- Family history: You are at greater risk if your mother had a heart attack before age 65, or your father before age 55.
- Smoking accounts for one-fifth of CVD deaths.
- Cholesterol levels: Increased total cholesterol, increased levels of low density lipoprotein (LDL) cholesterol greater than 130, low

levels (less than 35) of high density lipoprotein (HDL), and trig-lyceride levels of greater than 400 mg/dL increase the risk for CVD. With high cholesterol, there is a fatty deposit, or plaque, in blood vessels.

- People with hypertension or diabetes; and those who lead a sedentary lifestyle and are obese, are also at a greater risk of CVD.
- Stress: A relationship between stress and CVD has been established. The belief is that stress increases heart rate and blood pressure.

My Point of View

- Keep your blood pressure and diabetes under control.
- Keep your lipids and cholesterol levels under control. Limit your fat intake.
- Keep your weight under control. Keep your waist measurement less than 35 inches (40 inches for men.)
- Hormonal replacement therapy after menopause has been associated with a 35 to 50% decreased risk of CVD.
- Practice stress and depression management. The belief is that stress increases heart rate and blood pressure.
- Exercise regularly.
- Consider the use of baby aspirin. In a report published in January 2002, the US Preventive Services Task force "strongly" recommended that clinicians discuss the use of aspirin with adults who are at increased risk of heart disease. This would include men older than age 40, postmenopausal women and younger people with risk factors such as a family history of heart disease, or you have high cholesterol, diabetes, hypertension, or you smoke. Side effects of aspirin include increased risk of cerebral hemorrhage and gastrointestinal bleeding, so before taking any long-term medication, including aspirin, you should consult your health-care provider.
- If you smoke, quit!
- Use alcohol in moderation.
- *Please make sure that your family members, especially the men, know their blood pressure (and cholesterol levels).*

Osteoporosis

The Facts

Osteoporosis – loss of bone density of the vertebrae and the long bones, especially the hip, wrist and arm – is very common after menopause. What triggers bone loss in men is not clear. Women have a greater risk of osteoporosis than men because they have less bone to begin with. Women lose as much as 20% of their bone mass during the first 5 to 7 years after menopause. Low estrogen levels are the most important cause of bone loss in women.

Osteoporosis can cause loss of height and the outward curve of the upper spine, often cruelly called "dowager's hump." It also increases the risk of bone fractures from trivial accidents. An estimated ten million Americans now have bones that are porous enough to warrant a diagnosis of osteoporosis, causing a huge impact on the public's health.

Every year, women in the United States suffer at least 600,000 bone fractures directly caused by osteoporosis. One of six women will fracture a hip during their lifetime. The precise cause of osteoporosis is unknown, but studies show that inactivity and calcium deficiency are some of the precipitating factors. Up to 15% of women on hormone replacement therapy can still develop osteoporosis.

You are at a higher risk for osteoporosis if your ancestors came from Europe (especially northern Europe) or Asia. Other risk factors include being very thin, using steroids or anticonvulsive medication, smoking, alcohol abuse and lack of exercise. A recent study has shown that tooth loss is a possible sign of osteoporosis.

My Point of View

Regular weight-bearing exercises like walking, jogging, cycling and playing tennis – beginning no later than age 35 – can help prevent osteoporosis. Other preventive measures include smoking cessation, stress management, moderating the use of alcohol, caffeine and soft drinks, eating a balanced diet containing about 1500 mg of calcium a day and vitamin D, which helps the body use calcium more efficiently. Cheese, nonfat milk and yogurt, other milk products, sesame seeds, legumes and almonds are rich in calcium. Vitamin D is added to fluid milk. Phytoestrogens may also have a role in the prevention of osteoporosis.

Drugs for the prevention of osteoporosis include estrogen, biophos-phonates such as Alendronate, Raloxifene, and progesterone.

The diagnosis of osteoporosis is made by measuring the bone density (BMD). Screening should be reserved for high-risk perimenopausal women such are those with an x-ray suggestive of osteopenia, women receiving long-term steroid therapy, those with a history of eating disorders such as anorexia nervosa, and women diagnosed with primary asymptomatic hyperparathy-roidism. A baseline BMD should be ordered for women who choose not to undergo HRT at menopause.

Treatment of osteoporosis consists of ERT (estrogen replacement therapy), biophosphonate, calcitonin, and actonel. Adding androgens to ERT may build bone mass more effectively than estrogen alone.

Alzheimer's Disease

The Facts

Alzheimer's disease is the most common of disorders causing cognitive decline in old age, and it accounts for about 50% of all cases of dementia. In its early stages, Alzheimer's can be confused with depression, in that patients experience withdrawal, loss of concentration, memory failure, delusion, agitation, intellectual impairment, and anxiety. As the disease progresses, an individual may become extremely confused, unaware of her surroundings, disoriented, suspicious, paranoid, fearful, irritable, and even violent. During the latter stages, people may become unable to take care of themselves, socialize or communicate. The impact of an elderly parent with Alzheimer's is greater on women because they are usually the caretakers.

Most Alzheimer's occurs later in life, with a greater prevalence after age 65. Approximately 10% of Americans older than 65 have the disease; almost 50% of those sufferers are over the age of 85. Alzheimer's occurs more often among women than men, partially because women typically outlive men.

The cause of Alzheimer's disease is unknown. Multiple factors including environmental influences, nutritional deficiencies, and genetic factors may contribute to the disease. Some studies reveal that higher levels of education and intelligence are related to a *decreased risk* of Alzheimer's disease.

Possible causes of Alzheimer's disease:
- hypertension
- diabetes
- alcoholism
- a history of hypothyroidism, head trauma, hip fractures, myocardial infarction, or strokes
- having had general anesthesia
- estrogen deficiency

Alzheimer's disease prevention:
- If you smoke, here is another reason you should quit: Cigarette smoking causes small blood vessel damage that decreases oxygen to the brain.
- Regular exercise has been shown to improve memory in women with dementia.
- Stay active, be involved with life, and be a constant learner—use your brain!
- Antioxidants reduce the amount of debilitating free radicals in brain tissue
- Other strategies include the use of nonsteroidal anti-inflammatory medications such as ibuprofen.
- Women who take estrogen can slow age-related memory loss and possibly prevent Alzheimer's disease.

Women and Cancer

The Facts

In 2002, an estimated 267,300 Americans women are expected to die of cancer. African Americans have the highest incidence rates of cancer compared to other races. They are about 33% more likely to die of cancer than are whites and more than twice as likely to die than other races. Cancer is by far the leading cause of death among women aged 40 to 59 and among women aged 60 to 79. Cancer is a potential threat to women of any age. The most common cancers in women include lung, breast, colorectal, cervix, uterus, and skin.

Leading Causes of Death for US Women 1999

Heart disease	373,575
Cancer	264,006
Cerebrovascular Diseases	102,881

Estimated New Cancer Percentages for US Women 2002

Breast	31%
Lung	12%
Colon & Rectum	12%
Uterus	6%
Non-Hodgkin's Lymphoma	4%
Ovary	4%
Melanoma of the Skin	4%
Bladder	2%
Pancreas	2%
Thyroid	2%
All Other Sites	20%

Estimated Cancer Death Percentages for US Women 2002

Lung	25%
Breast	15%
Colon & Rectum	11%
Pancreas	6%
Ovary	5%
Non-Hodgkin's Lymphoma	4%
Leukemia	4%

Uterus	2%
Brain	2%
Multiple Myeloma	2%
All Other Body Sites	23%

Source: American Cancer Society

Lung Cancer

The Facts

More American women die of lung cancer than from any other type of cancer. Smoking accounts for 90% of lung cancer in men and 85% in women. The American Cancer Society projects that lung cancer will kill 90,200 men and 79,200 women in 2002. About 400,000 people die in the United States each year from smoking-related disease, about 100,000 of them from second-hand smoke. *Since 1960 the smoking-related death rate has risen 104% in men and 452% in women.* Unfortunately, there is no effective routine screen for lung cancer. Studies have showed that screening allows lung cancer to be diagnosed in an earlier stage with better survival in a screened population. However there has been no decrease in mortality in those screened.

Smoking is the single most preventable cause of illness and premature death. Avoiding smoking can greatly lower the risk of lung cancer, as well as heart disease, emphysema and other forms of chronic lung disease, cervical, bladder, and breast cancer. If you're pregnant and still smoke, use alcohol or take other drugs, you run a greater risk of damaging your unborn child. You're also at a higher risk of premature delivery, having a child with low birth weight (which has its own hazards), and with physical and mental abnormalities.

Up to 35,000 deaths from heart attacks in the United States each year are thought to be caused by "passive" smoking. Secondhand smoke is responsible for 150,000 to 300,000 ailments in children per year. There is a 30% higher risk of lung cancer in women whose spouse is a smoker.

My Point of View

It is your right to ask people around you to refrain from smoking. Do not allow others to smoke in close proximity to you, either in the car, in your home, or in enclosed outdoor areas.

Nicotine is a highly addictive substance, and the habit of smoking is seductive, but people can still find the courage and willpower to quit if they are motivated. First, you must *want* to quit, then find a way to quit that fits within your lifestyle. Just because you try and fail once or twice does not mean that you will never succeed. You *can* do it. Just keep trying! Please.

The willingness to quit, together with a smoking cessation program, the use of nicotine replacement products as well prescription drugs such as Zyban are associated with a higher rate of success.

Breast Cancer

The Facts

Breast cancer is the most common noncutaneous (non-skin) cancer in women, and is the leading cause of death among women aged 40 to 59. In the United States, breast cancer is the second leading cause of cancer deaths in women. An estimated 203,500 women will be diagnosed with breast cancer in 2002, and of that total, 40,000 will die of the disease. An estimated 1,500 men will be diagnosed with breast cancer and 400 will die of the disease.

This type of cancer is more common in older women, but can strike women of any age. The leading risk factors for breast cancer are simply being female and getting older. About 75% of women diagnosed with breast cancer have no identifiable risk factors. It has been suggested that if a woman's mother, sister, half-sister, or daughter has had breast cancer, she is at a higher-than-average risk of developing the disease. Other circumstances correlating with higher risk include being Caucasian, being older than 50 years of age, not having given birth to a child, becoming a mother for the first time after the age of 30, the use of long-term estrogen replacement therapy (ERT) and long-term estrogen/progestin replacement therapy (HRT)

Others at higher risk include women who started their period early or entered menopause very late (over the age of 55); very obese women, women with extra weight distributed in the upper body and stomach, rather than in the hips and thighs; women with a history of benign disease confirmed by biopsy; women with a high socioeconomic status; women on estrogen replacement therapy after menopause; women who have been on the Pill for a very long period; women with a specific genetic mutation, such as BRCA-1 and BRCA-2 genes, which increases susceptibility; and women with at least 75% of breast tissue so dense that interpretation of a mammogram is problematic. Black women are less likely to develop breast cancer than white women, but they are more likely to die from it.

Fortunately, 90% of breast cancers that are detected early – with a mammogram while they're too small to be felt – are curable, meaning the woman lived for five or more additional years after treatment.

My Point of View

Please follow these steps to reduce your risk of breast cancer:

- **Monthly Breast Self-Exam**

  You should perform a breast self-exam monthly and note any change – a mass, skin changes, or abnormal nipple discharge. The best time to examine your breast is a week after the start of your menstrual period. If you do not menstruate, choose an easy-to-remember date, such the first of the month. In front of a mirror, first with your hands on your hips, and then with your arms held above your head, note any retraction of the skin or change in the contour of each breast. In the shower, raise one arm and use the fingers of the opposite hand to feel the breast for any masses or unusual thickness. Do this for each breast. After you're out of the shower, lie down on your back with a folded towel below one shoulder. Put one hand under your head and feel the breast with the three middle fingers of the opposite hand. Using a circular and continuous motion, examine the whole breast, beginning around the nipple. Without lifting the fingers, enlarge the circle until you have examined the entire breast. Do not forget to check the armpit for any unusual mass. Now perform the same sequence on the other breast.

- **Yearly Clinical Breast Examination**

Have your doctor perform an annual breast exam. During your annual exam, demonstrate your self-exam technique to your doctor to be sure you are doing it correctly.

- **Regular Mammogram**

A mammogram is an exam of the breast with low-dose x-rays. Mammograms allow detection of a breast cancer in a very early stage, even before you or your doctor can feel its presence. It has been indicated that screening women aged 50 and older with annual mammograms leads to a decrease in mortality from breast cancer. But, mammograms are not perfect since they may miss from 10 to 15% of breast cancers. That is why if a woman discovers a new lump in her breast, it should be biopsied (a sample of it removed for laboratory examination), even though her mammogram was negative. More than 50% of women who have had a mammogram complain of some type of discomfort. If the discomfort persists, take a mild analgesic like Tylenol. Sometimes the skin is slightly discolored following a mammogram, but this usually disappears in a few days.

Many studies have demonstrated that mammograms are the best way to detect early breast cancer. Each woman should have a mammogram starting at age 40 and every year or every other year until age 50. After age 50, a mammogram should be taken every year. If you have a personal history of breast cancer, or if you have had an abnormal breast biopsy result, you need to have a mammogram every year thereafter. If your mother, sister, or daughter had breast cancer before age 50, you need to have a mammogram every year starting at age 35. If your mother, sister, or daughter had breast cancer at age 50 or older, you need to have a mammogram every year starting at age 40. Similar to previous studies of screening mammography, comparison of diagnostic mammograms with prior examinations increases the cancer detection rate in subsets of patients, including women who have undergone lumpectomies, according to study results presented at the American Roentgen Ray Society's annual meeting.

Other breast cancer prevention measures:

• Regular exercise: Women who exercise regularly are less likely to develop breast cancer.

• Smoking cessation: Women who smoke cigarettes quadruple their risk of breast cancer.

• Consume alcohol with moderation: In one study, women who consumed two to five alcoholic beverages (wine, beer, and hard liquor) per day demonstrated a 41% increased risk of developing invasive breast cancer. Women who drank one alcoholic beverage per day were also found to be at increased risk.

• Keep your weight under control: Obese women are more likely to have breast cancer then thin women.

• Eating a healthy low-fat diet and a diet rich in fish oil, and omega-3 fatty acids has been associated with lower breast cancer rates.

• Drugs such as Tamoxifen and Raloxifen have been shown in some studies to decrease the rate of breast cancer. These drugs, especially tamoxifen, do have some serious side effects including blood clots and uterine cancer. There is a need for more extensive assessment before these drugs are given to healthy women.

Colorectal Cancer

The Facts

Colorectal (colon and rectal) cancer is the third leading cause of cancer death for women, most often striking those over age 50. An estimated 57,300 women will be diagnosed with colon cancer and 18,400 with rectal cancer in 2002, and of that total, 25,000 will die of colon cancer and 3,800 of rectal cancer.

Black women are more likely to develop colorectal cancers than are women of any other racial or ethnic group. Unfortunately, the majority of women are seen with advanced-stage disease.

Guidelines for screening for colorectal cancer of average-risk individuals include:

- An annual fecal occult blood testing (FOBT) should be performed during the rectal exam to check the stool for signs of blood.
- In addition to the digital rectal exam at the office (DRE) six samples (two samples from three consecutive specimens) should be collected at home and returned to the doctor's office. Over-the-counter fecal-blood kits can sometimes be inaccurate.

  Observe these recommendations before performing the FOBT test at home:
  - Non-steroidal anti-inflammatory drugs such as aspirin (more than one adult aspirin per day), naproxen, or ibuprofen, should be avoided for seven days prior to collecting the samples, since they can cause gastrointestinal bleeding.
  - Red meat, and vitamin C in excess of 250 mg from supplements or citrus fruits should be avoided for three days.
  - Other foods that can cause a false-positive chemical reaction are: turnips, cauliflower, radishes, and melons.
  - You should postpone the test if you are experiencing bleeding gums, bleeding hemorrhoids, or if you are menstruating.
- Annual FOBT plus flexible sigmoidoscopy every five years. Sigmoidoscopy is the visualization of the rectum and the lower portion of the colon. During the exam, the walls of the colon are examined and a sample of tissues (biopsy) can be taken if anything unusual is noted.
- Annual FOBT plus double contrast barium enema (DCBE) every five years.
- Colonoscopy every 10 years. During colonoscopy, the rectum and the full length of the colon are examined. For women over age 40 who have a history of inflammatory bowel disease such as ulcerative colitis and Crohn's disease, polyps in the colon, or a family history of colon cancer, a colonoscopy should be performed. An alternative would be to have a sigmoidoscopy plus a barium enema.
- If you observe any change in bowel movements, any rectal bleed-

ing or blood in the stool, you should consult your health-care provider. If there's a history of this disease in your family, your health-care provider should be informed of this too.

My Point of View

I personally do not recommend a sigmoidoscopy to my patients. Since a sigmoidoscopy only offers partial visualization of the colon, to me it's like having a mammogram of only one breast when screening for breast cancer.

Cervical Cancer

The Facts

Testing for cancer of the cervix is a good example of how prevention and early detection make life better. *Cervical cancer is the most frequent deadly cancer in developing countries where prevention is lacking.* The Pap test to screen for cervical cancer was introduced in 1950, and soon became widely used in the United States. The result? With early detection and treatment, the number of deaths from cervical cancer dropped from 8,487 in 1960 to 4,100 in 2002, while the size of the sexually active female population increased considerably.

The Risks

The risk for developing cervical cancer increases:

- With having sexual intercourse at a very young age and with many partners.
- If you or your sex partner have or have had multiple sex partners.
- If you have a history of genital warts or HPV (Human Papilloma Virus) infection. Certain strains of HPV have been associated with cervical cancer.

My Point of View

- Warning Signs: Unfortunately, by the time a woman is experiencing symptoms of irregular bleeding caused by a cervical cancer, it means that the cancer is very advanced. *Thus the rationale for routine Pap tests.* According to the College of American Pathologists, early detection by Pap smears followed by appropriate treatment has led to a 70% reduction in the incidence of the disease in the United States. It is now a less frequent cause of women's deaths than cancers of the lungs, breast, colon, ovary and uterus.
- Early Detection: Early detection includes submitting to a regular pelvic exam and Pap tests every 1 to 3 years according to your risks. According to a report in *Science,* Pap smears should remain the primary method of cervical cancer screening.

Ovarian Cancer

The Facts

More women die of ovarian cancer than any other gynecologic cancer. Ovarian cancer is the second most common gynecologic cancer and the leading cause of cancer deaths in women. About 13,900 women in the US are expected to die from ovarian cancer in 2002. Three out of four women with ovarian cancer will show advanced-stage disease, with a 5-year survival of only 20%. Unfortunately, there is no proven routine screening test for ovarian cancer. Both CA125 and ultrasound have been found to be inadequate. However, they should be considered for women at high risk.

The Risks

The risks include:

- Aging – especially if you are over 50.
- If you have a history of ovarian cancer.
- If you have had breast cancer.

- If you have a first-degree relative with ovarian cancer. Those with 2 first-degree relatives with ovarian cancer have up to 50% risk. These women may have a mutation in BRCA1 or BRCA2 gene and should be referred for genetic counseling and consider a prophylactic removal of their ovaries after childbearing is completed.

My Point of View

Women with ovarian cancer usually have vague symptoms that may not seem to be related to the disease. You should be aware if you have:

- persistent digestive problems including gas, nausea, and stomach discomfort.
- abdominal bloating, a lump, swelling and/or pain.
- abnormal vaginal bleeding.

Uterine (Endometrial) Cancer

The Facts

Uterine cancer is the most common gynecologic cancer in women. It usually begins in the endometrium, the interior lining of the uterus.

The Risks

The risks include:

- Aging – especially if you are over 50.
- If you are obese.
- If you have irregular periods.
- If you are taking estrogen replacement therapy without the use of a progesterone or progestin.
- If you have menopause after 52.
- If you take the drug Tamoxifen.

My Point of View

Warning signs include irregular vaginal bleeding, spotting or discharge, especially if you are over 35 or on hormone replacement therapy (HRT) and/or lower abdominal discomfort.

Less common gynecological cancers include cancer of the vagina, fallopian tubes and vulva. The risk of these cancers increases with age, in women with a history of HPV and a history of gynecologic cancer, especially cervical cancer.

Skin Cancer

The Facts

Skin cancer is the most common cancer in the US. Approximately 1 million people develop skin cancer each year and it accounts for 2% of all cancer deaths. There are three types of skin cancer: basal cell carcinoma - the most common, squamous cell carcinoma and melanona. Melanoma accounts for 75% of skin cancer death. About 4,700 men and 2,700 women are expected to die from it in 2002. Fortunately, 90% of melanomas are visible to the naked eye.

The Risks

Skin cancers are more common in people who are, or were anytime in their life, exposed to the sun for a long time and those who have gotten sunburned. They're even more common in women with light skin.

My Point of View

Any unusual skin lesions or changes in a birthmark or mole should be checked by a health-care provider.

You should avoid too much exposure to the sun, especially midday sun. Wear clothing that covers most parts of the body and use at least an SPF 15 sunblock to protect exposed skin. Tanning salon exposure is as dangerous as the real sun. In a study that appeared in the Journal of the National Cancer Institute, researchers found that people who used tanning devices were 1 ½ to 2 ½ times more likely to have skin cancer than were people who did not use the device. The risk was highest for those who first used tanning devices before the age of 20.

For further help, use the UV Index now given in many daily newspapers. This index translates the day's amount of cancer-related ultraviolet (UV) radiation into safe tanning minutes for your skin type.

☀☀☀

OTHER HEALTH PRECAUTIONS

Choose the Right Birth Control for You

Today, more birth control methods are available than ever before. However, women of all reproductive age groups are still being confronted with unintended pregnancy and subsequent abortions, mostly because of not using birth control.

Hormone-based birth-control methods including "the Pill," *(on May 9, 2000, the Pill turned 40!),* the skin implant Norplant, the injection Depo-Provera, Lunelle, the IUD (intrauterine device), and sterilization, are most effective. They are far more effective than methods that must be used each time you have intercourse, which include the male and female condom, diaphragm, spermicides, films, cervical cap, rhythm method, withdrawal, or natural family planning.

The methods that include the use of spermicides, especially those containing Nonoxynol-9 (N9), have a better chance of protecting against some forms of STDs (sexually transmitted disease).

In choosing a birth-control method, you must evaluate how it will affect your life. Will it diminish the spontaneity of lovemaking? Are you comfortable enough to insert birth-control devices before having sex? What about your partner? If the birth-control method must be used each time prior to intercourse, is it effective in preventing pregnancy? Does it also protect against sexually transmitted disease (STDs)? Except for abstinence, no birth-control method is 100% effective against pregnancy, HIV (the AIDS virus), or other types of STDs.

Emergency Contraception (EC), or "Morning After Pill"

Emergency contraception, which includes contraceptive pills and emergency IUD insertion, can prevent pregnancy after intercourse, before pregnancy is established. I am talking about measures that can prevent pregnancy by preventing maturation of the fertilized egg.

An estimated 3 million pregnancies occur each year in the US and as many as 700,000 result in abortions. Emergency contraception could prevent as many as 1.8 million of these pregnancies.

You may need emergency contraception, if:

- You had intercourse and used no contraception.
- You were using a condom and it slipped or broke.
- Your diaphragm dislodged.
- You were raped.

If you think you may need emergency contraception, contact your health-care provider as soon as possible after the sexual activity, but preferably no later than 72 hours afterward. Or, you can call 888-NOT-2-LATE, or check www.NOT-2late.com to hear information about how you can prevent pregnancy after sex. You may also ask you health-care provider about giving you an advance prescription for emergency contraception and have it on hand in case you need it.

Abortion

Unfortunately, some women rely on abortion as a type of birth control. It is also relied on when a birth-control method has failed. Types of abortion performed depend on the length of the pregnancy.

In the first trimester (the first 12 weeks after the last menstrual period), the most-used procedure is vacuum aspiration, in which a suction instrument removes the embryo or fetus and the placenta.

RU 486, an abortion-inducing pill, is used during the first six weeks after the last menstrual period. This treatment is just becoming generally available in the United States, but has been fully available in France, the United

Kingdom and some other nations.

In the second trimester several procedures are used. If the pregnancy is already 13-16 weeks, dilation and evacuation can be used. This procedure is similar to vacuum aspiration. If the pregnancy is 16-24 weeks, the more common procedure is induction of labor by injection of a fluid – salt (saline) solution or prostaglandin hormones – into the amniotic sac. Hysterotomy (incision into the uterus) and in extreme cases, hysterectomy can also be performed.

Abortion should not be considered a form of birth control. It is an invasive procedure that years later, may have serious emotional and physical repercussions, including sterility. It is to be treated seriously.

The Benefits of Planned Pregnancies

Advanced pregnancy planning is optimal for both mother and baby because of medical, psychological, economic and social benefits. A planned pregnancy offers financial stability for a woman and her partner. These benefits are even of greater concern for an adolescent woman, since it can be associated with poverty and or long-term socioeconomic disadvantage for both the mother and her child.

The outcome of a pregnancy depends greatly on your state of health and your lifestyle before you ever become pregnant. Proper pre-conceptual and prenatal care go hand-in-hand with having a healthy baby, regardless of your age.

The best beginning is to take proper care of yourself even before you try to become pregnant. The fertilized egg (the embryo) draws all its nutrients from the endometrium – the thick, blood-filled lining of the uterus. The embryo implants itself upon the endometrium and begins to develop into a baby ready for birth approximately 40 weeks later. The nutrients supplied by the endometrium come directly from what you put into your own body.

Many birth defects occur during the first two weeks of pregnancy, often at a time when a woman does not know she is pregnant. Birth defects can be hereditary, but can also be caused by toxic substances, viral infections, nutritional deficiencies, radiation from X-rays, some prescription medicines, drugs, and alcohol. While the mother's health and activities can help to prevent many birth defects, some defects are beyond the mother's, or anyone's, control. If there is a family history of birth defects or inherited disorders, check with your health-care provider about genetic testing before you try to conceive.

Before becoming pregnant, also have your dentist take care of any cavities, since the body reroutes minerals used for tooth maintenance to the unborn child.

Hopefully, you already have a good relationship with the health-care provider who will care for you while you're pregnant. Discuss your respective views on childbirth to see if they agree. If you don't agree, it may be appropriate to find another health-care provider. If you have any medical problems, now is the time to get them resolved or under control. Don't wait until after you become pregnant.

It is a good idea to be in good physical health and within five pounds of your ideal weight when you become pregnant. You should stop taking all over-the-counter medications, except folic acid found in vitamin B-complex or multivitamin supplements. The US Public Health Service recommends that all women of childbearing age consume at least 0.4 mg of folic acid each day. Taking multivitamin supplements with folic acid during the three months before becoming pregnant has been demonstrated to reduce the risk of neural-tube defects. If you must take prescribed medications, talk to your health-care provider to make sure they are not known to cause birth defects. If necessary, your health-care provider may be able to provide safer alternatives.

Avoid all toxic substances like alcohol and other drugs. Alcohol can reduce the chance of getting pregnant when you want to. If you smoke, this is a good time to quit. Taking herbs or over-the counter supplements, which many people consider harmless, can be risky.

Make sure you are vaccinated against or are immune to Rubella (German measles). If a woman contracts Rubella during pregnancy, especially during the first three months, it could cause serious birth defects. Because of the potential risk to the developing fetus, vaccines should be administered as part of the pre-conception evaluation.

If you are taking the Pill, switch to a barrier method of birth control (such as condoms together with foam,) for at least three cycles before trying to become pregnant. It may take up to six to eight weeks for some women who have been on the Pill to begin having a regular cycle. Once your cycle becomes regular, it will be much easier to determine when you become pregnant, and to calculate your due date.

There is a perception that women can delay childbearing while having a career. You need to know that a woman's fertility rate declines after age 35. Becoming pregnant later in life has increased, but there are risks that should be evaluated with your health-care provider.

Sexually Transmitted Disease (STD) Prevention

The most common STDs in the United States are chlamydia, herpes, gonorrhea, syphilis, genital warts, trichomoniasis, hepatitis B, hepatitis C, and HIV (human immunodeficiency virus) or AIDS (Acquired Immunodeficiency Syndrome). HIV is the virus responsible for AIDS. Several other diseases occur but are less common. Granuloma inguinale and chancroid are characterized by painful genital ulcers and the formation of pus in the lymph nodes of the groin. Lymphogranuloma venereum, caused by a member of the chlamydia group of organisms, creates a sore, inflammation, and pus in the lymph system. Two insect-caused skin diseases can also be transmitted sexually – scabies (caused by mites), and pediculosis pubis (caused by lice).

Women disproportionately bear the long-term consequences of STDs. According to a study financed by the National Institute of Allergy and Infectious Diseases, women are twice as likely as men to contact gonorrhea, hepatitis B, and other STDs, with minority women disproportionately affected.

According to a report published in the Journal of the American Medical Association in March 2001, women now represent almost 1 in 5 cases of AIDS in the US compared to about 1 in 15 AIDS cases in 1986. Prevention of sexually transmitted disease also improves the quality of life. Sexual promiscuity these days could be a matter of life and death. Abstinence is the only certain way of preventing such diseases. But staying with one sexual partner and using latex condoms can greatly lower the risk of getting HIV (the AIDS virus) and other diseases.

But the use of condoms is not always protective against STDs. Nonoxynol-9 N-9 when used as spermicides are effective in preventing pregnancy, particularly when used with a diaphragm. However, one study found that N-9 did not protect against HIV infection and may have caused more transmission. The women in that study who used N-9 gel became infected with HIV at approximately a 50% higher rate than women who used the placebo gel.

All sexually active women with male partners need protection from unwanted pregnancy, as well as protection against STDs.

Risk factors for STDs include:

- Being sexually active
- Having a history with a STD
- Having multiple sexual partners
- Having a partner who has or had multiple sexual partners
- Having a partner with a STD
- Using the Pill
- Having an IUD
- Previous treatment for pelvic inflammatory disease.

Some questions that need to be answered before engaging in intercourse with a new partner:

- How many sexual partners did he have in the past year?
- Did he use a condom with every sexual partner?
- Do you know your partner's sexual habits?
- Has your partner had any blood transfusions?
- Has your partner had any STDs?
- Does your partner intend to be faithful?

Most of these diseases can be prevented by changing lifestyles, principally through abstinence or maintaining a monogamous relationship, and avoiding sexual contact with people who have genital sores or high-risk lifestyles.

I recommend to my patients that, when they meet a new partner, regardless of how clean and healthy he may appear, they should not engage in intercourse until he has been tested for the HIV virus. Also, they should remember that it may take up to one year for an infected person to have a positive test. Some men may be reluctant to get tested. I tell my patients that if that man really cares for them, he should understand and cooperate.

It can be very difficult for women to ask a partner to use a condom. Women need to stop seeing themselves as victims and discover how powerful they really are. It is important to take charge of your sexuality, enjoy sex, and protect yourself at the same time. Use condoms, and get tested!

Be Aware of Toxic Substances

Toxic chemicals are a part of your life. Aerosols, artificial sweeteners, cosmetics, dyes, inks, paints, pesticides, pharmaceuticals, plastics, synthetic fabrics — our homes are overflowing with chemicals. In fact, the domestic chemical industry is now worth a staggering $1.5 trillion per year.

- Seventy thousand new chemicals have been introduced since World War II. 250 billion pounds of synthetic chemicals are produced each year in the US according to the California Public Interest Research Group. *We are the first generation to grow up with such extremely high levels of chemicals in our homes.*

- Now thousands of these chemicals are appearing on the shelves of your grocery store – in products to clean your clothes, your floor, your hair, your teeth, etc. And by being on sale in the store, you'd like to think they are safe.

- According to the US National Research Council, no information of toxic effects is available for 79% of the synthetic chemicals listed by the US Environmental Protection Agency (EPA).

- *Chemicals in your home may interact with each other to give off a toxicity that would not exist in either of the products individually. And, certain chemicals become toxic only after the body's metabolism processes them.*

- Chemicals are taken into your system not only from inhalation or through the food you eat, but also by absorption through the pores of your skin.

- "Of chemicals commonly found in homes, 150 have been linked to allergies, birth defects, cancer and psychological abnormalities." – *Consumer Products Safety Commission*

- "After analyzing 2,983 chemicals used in personal care products, 884 were found to be toxic." – *National Institute of Occupational Safety and Health*

- The EPA reports that toxic chemicals found in every home – from cleaning products to personal care products – are three times more likely to cause cancer than airborne pollutants.

- *EPA statistics show that women who work at home are 55% more likely to develop cancer than women working away from the home, because of household cleaners.*

- Children have higher respiratory rates than adults, so they inhale three times the amount of contaminants, and they can't filter toxins as well as adults do.

- Infants and young children can be more vulnerable to chemicals because pollutants can impact their developing systems, resulting in lifelong effects. We are just beginning to see how toxins in children's lives are taking a toll – we have a higher rate of children with cancer and learning disabilities than ever before, and SIDS was only recognized after the introduction of synthetic chemicals.

It's official: Staying home is hazardous to your health!

- In one five-year study, the EPA reported that a number of homes had chemical levels that were 70 times higher inside the home than outside.

- These levels of indoor air pollutants are of particular concern because it is estimated that *most people, including children, spend as much as 90% of their time indoors.*

- In recent years, comparative risk studies performed by EPA and its Science Advisory Board (SAB) have consistently ranked *indoor air pollution* among the top five environmental risks to public health.

- Exposure to toxins can aggravate symptoms of allergy and asthma and compromise the immune system.

- Over a long period of time, toxic products can contribute to the development of cancer, birth defects, genetic changes and other illness.

- If the EPA knows all this, why doesn't the government do something? It has tried, but – *surprise* – economic interests prevail. Many products don't require labeling, and products like pesticides only have to include the active ingredients, even though inert ingredients may account for 99% of the product!

- At present, many chemicals used in cosmetics, pesticides, and other products do not require full safety testing before they are allowed to be marketed and used by millions of consumers.
- Billions of dollars are spent every year to convince us through advertising that they are necessary and will enhance our lives.

What can we do?

- Be an informed consumer – Maintain ingredient awareness and be aware of what substances, from pesticides to cleaners, pose threats in your household.
- There are healthy alternatives. Find conscientious companies producing safer non-toxic products.
- Use environmentally-safe non-caustic cleaners and personal health care products that do not leave toxic residues.
- Collectively we'll make a big difference when we start spending our dollars with the companies that care about our health and the environment.
- More information about this is available through the State or Federal Occupational Safety and Health Administration.

Vision Screening

Glaucoma – damage to the optic nerve caused by elevated pressure within the eye – is the leading cause of preventable blindness. Glaucoma is present in 5% of the population age 40 and above. Loss of vision due to glaucoma is permanent and irreversible. So it is very important to discover glaucoma early and treat it adequately. A simple and painless test can easily diagnose the presence or absence of glaucoma.

Starting at age 40, you should have this test performed by an optometrist, a family health-care provider, or an ophthalmologist on a regular basis.

Dental Hygiene

A visit to the dentist every six months for teeth cleaning and to rule out dental and gum disease is a must for every adult and child. Researchers have linked gum disease to diabetes, heart disease, pre-term births and osteoporosis. An Italian study found that people with good teeth and gums live a longer and happier life. Watch for early gum disease – signs include gums that bleed when you brush you teeth, tender, red or swollen gums and persistent bad breath. Pregnant women with moderate to severe periodontal disease have an increased risk of giving birth to a pre-term infant.

Immunizations

A tetanus booster shot should be given once between age 14-16, then every 10 years. Residents of chronic-care facilities and those with blood disorders, diabetes or renal diseases should receive the influenza vaccine annually starting in their twenties. Beginning at age 50, every woman should receive the influenza vaccine annually, and the pneumoccocal vaccine once.

Anyone who may come in contact with human blood or blood products, or with people at risk for sexually transmitted disease, should be immunized against the liver disease hepatitis B.

Guns

Many people have guns for "protection." But for each use of a gun against an intruder, there are 100 gun-related deaths among children and other family members. Family disputes, children's curiosity and accidents can all lead to death or serious injury if a gun is nearby.

IF YOU HAVE A GUN, KEEP IT OUT OF REACH OF CHILDREN.

Car Driver and Passenger Safety

In year 2000 there were 41,821 automobile-related deaths and nearly 4.3 million injuries in the US. The simple act of wearing a seat belt while driving can avoid grave injuries in case of an accident. Parents should make it a practice to place their children in proper car seats.

And, of course, never drink and drive!

It's Your Body

Consult a health-care provider in case of a nagging cough, persistent hoarse voice, problems with swallowing, unusual bleeding or discharge, any unusual lump or discharge from the breast, or a sore that does not heal.

Cancer-related checkups should be performed every three years from ages 20 to 29 and annually after age 40. The checkups should include examination for cancer of the lymph nodes, oral cavity, skin, and ovaries.

Home remedies can help with some mild forms of illness. But serious illness, like cancer, calls for the attention of a specialist and hospital treatment. Please pay attention to symptoms that do not go away, and take the steps to put yourself in competent hands.

YOU AND YOUR DOCTOR

In these times of managed care insurance, many health-care providers have time constraints when it comes to interactions with their patients. Patients may find themselves disappointed, complaining that some of their questions have not been answered. A good patient/provider relationship requires mutual effort and respect.

The days are over when women depended completely on their health-care providers to learn about their own health, and decisions were made for them. Women are getting their information from television, magazines, newspapers, support groups and Internet websites. Sometimes, a patient hears about a new treatment even before the information reaches me.

These days, informed women want to be part of the decision-making and I welcome this approach. Although the decision to be made is yours, you need to know that your knowledge is limited. You should be aware that medical news coverage, or the Internet, often focuses on specific, isolated topics, and will not include all the information needed to make individualized choices.

If you are a woman of an ethnic minority, you need to know that most research results from clinical studies are skewed because they either do not include women like you or the numbers of minority women included are usually so small that the findings are not viable. The results, though, do relate to you indirectly and should be considered as you make your choice. That is why the help of a trusted and knowledgeable health-care provider is needed - even though you may have to go out of your HMO system and pay out-of-pocket!

Preparing for Your Doctor Visit

No douching, or using any vaginal cream if you plan to go to see your doctor and be checked for an abnormal discharge. If you have any vaginal itching, are experiencing an abnormal vaginal discharge, or are still menstruating, a Pap smear will not be performed.

Optimizing Your Doctor Visit

- Be knowledgeable about your medical as well as your own family history (blood related only).
- Have a written list of the names of all medications you take, along with the dosage, what it is for and how many times a day it is taken. This should include any over-the-counter items including herbs, vitamins, and other supplements.
- Have a list of any allergies to medications, their exact name, and the type of reaction.
- Don't forget the type of surgeries and dates – including plastic surgeries such as breast implants.

- Mention any alternative treatment that you are undergoing such as acupuncture, chiropractic manipulation or chelation therapy.

- If you have a new problem, be direct about what you have been experiencing, especially how long and how severe. (For example, if 0 represents normal and 10 represents severe, choose a number that corresponds to the severity of your sickness.) Mention any medication, home remedy, herbs you've taken for relief, what makes it worse, and what makes it better.

- If you are seeing the health-care provider for a recurrent chronic problem, you should mention how often it occurred in the past, what kind of medications or therapy you have tried, which one worked and which one did not.

- Ask for the diagnosis in lay terms, explanations about the chosen treatment, risks, alternatives, and cost.

- Make your follow-up appointment, and follow all recommendations.

- For non-emergencies, take time to investigate on your own.

- For something serious, you may want to get a second and even a third opinion.

Follow-up Visit: Be Proactive

- Keep a log of any symptoms or changes since your last visit.

- Consider taking someone with you if you feel that your situation or your doctor's explanation is complicated for you to understand.

- Have a written list of questions.

Screening Exams to Detect Early Disease

Medical imaging screening exams such as total body CT scans and MRIs are aggressively being advertised in the media. Advertisements say that if a test is normal, you walk away with complete peace of mind. I am concerned about the indiscriminate use of medical imaging, the risks of both positive examinations and the false reassurance that comes with a negative examination.

If you have no symptoms and seek to detect a hidden disease, or if you have symptoms of an illness, medical imaging is an integrative part of making a diagnosis. However, it should be done in conjunction with a history, complete physical examination and laboratory data.

What You Can Do To Stay Informed

Be proactive. Congress makes health-care decisions every day that will affect you, including funding for research, treatment and cure for diseases related to woman's health such as breast, cervical cancer, and osteoporosis, insurance coverage for prescription drug, programs and laws to help abused women, health coverage for uninsured and underinsured women.

The American College of Obstetrician and Gynecologists (ACOG), of which I am a fellow, is a national medical specialty society that represents women's health care. Over 41,000 ob-gyns like me have worked with Congress on many issues in the past that are beneficial to women. Visit ACOG's website at www.acog.org and click on *Contact Congress*, which will take you to ACOG's Legislative Action Center. From there, you can:

- Discover the issues that most affect your health.
- Learn about issues and legislation that will affect you and your family.
- See how your Members of Congress vote on women's health issues.
- E-mail your Members of Congress and let them know what matters to you.

LIFETIME ROUTINE CHECKUP LIST

Test or Procedure	*How often*

I. General Heath

Blood Glucose	Age 45+: every 3 years
Blood Pressure	Annually; more frequently if over 140/90
Breast Self-Exam	Monthly, starting at age 20
Breast Clinical Exam	Every 3 years, ages 20-39 and yearly starting at age 40
Cholesterol	Every five years beginning at age 20, and more frequently if abnormal
Dental Checkup	Every 6 months
Electrocardiogram	As directed by your health-careprovider
Eye Exam	Age 40: baseline exam; 40-64: every 2-4 years; 65+: every 1-2 years
Hearing Test	Test if hearing problem or loss is suspected or as directed by your health-care provider
Mammography	Every one to two years from age 40, yearly beginning at age 50
Pap Test & Pelvic Exam	All women who are or have been sexually active or have reached age

18 – 21 should have a yearly Pap test and pelvic examination. After three or more consecutive normal Pap tests, it may be performed less frequently at the discretion of your health care provider.

STD's   At the discretion of you and your health care provider

TSH   Every 5 years, starting at age 40

II. Colon Cancer Screen
One of these schedules:

Fecal occult blood (FOBT)   Yearly, starting at age 50.
or
Colonoscopy   Every 10 years, starting at age 50

or
Double contrast barium enema Every 5 years, starting at
(DCBE)   age 50.

III. Vaccines

Hepatitis B vaccine   Three shots if you are sexually active and at risk

Influenza vaccine   Yearly, starting at age 55.

Tetanus-diphtheria booster   Every 10 years.

IV. Bone Mineral Density Test (BMD)

Note:
                                    At menopause, if you are not
                                    on estrogen therapy

- If you are a black woman 55 years or older and have never been on HRT, you should have a baseline BMD and repeat it every two to three years.

- If you are a postmenopausal Caucasian, Asian, Hispanic, or Native American and have never been on HRT, you should have a baseline BMD and repeat it every two to three years.

- If you are 60 years or older and have been on HRT, or have decided not to continue with HRT, you may want to have a baseline BMD and repeat it every two to three years.

- Also, according to the National Osteoporosis Foundation in collaboration with nine other medical organizations, all white women over the age of 65 should have a BMD test.

❦

CONCLUDING THOUGHTS ON PHYSICAL HEALTH

There is an explosion of information on the Internet and it can be a great tool for obtaining medical information. But as with everything else in life, there are always advantages and disadvantages. One outstanding advantage is that from the comfort of her home, a woman can pore over highly technical medical journals as well as peruse different sites that provide health information.

The downside is that with all this information available, some of it can be harmful and misleading to the general public. It can create anxiety making a person believe that they may have a certain illness when the presenting symptoms are common to many other illnesses. Those prone to suggestion may go overboard – patients misdiagnosing themselves, discontinuing their prescribed medications, and switching to some "alternative/natural" treatments, which have not been proven to be effective, and in some cases may even be harmful.

Chat rooms on various websites allow those with a certain illness or issue to collectively hear first-hand about another person's situation, how they are being treated, as well as discuss different coping mechanisms. It saves time rather than having to physically attend a support group. The major advantage of such sites is that they offer a Q&A section, enabling people to ask sensitive questions that, otherwise, they may not have the courage to ask a physician face-to-face.

The disadvantage is that in some cases the information you get through chat rooms may be skewed and cause you to believe you are worse off than you really are. A major pitfall with any information medium is the need to distinguish between objective information and advertisement. Regarding Dr. C. Everett Koop's website, the former Surgeon General was criticized for not properly disclosing his financial ties to various products he is promoting. Other sites have been criticized for "blurring the line between editorial content and advertising," creating a conflict of interest.

Online drugstores may appear to be a bargain, but can be deceptive. A number of them turned out to cost about 10% more than a regular pharmacy, due to the added expense of shipping and handling. Medications sold over the Internet also may come from overseas sites and may be of inferior quality. And to make matters worse, insurance companies generally do not reimburse for drugs bought via the Internet.

Getting the wrong information or the wrong medication can be very dangerous. There is no way of knowing if an individual proffering medical advice is, in reality, a qualified physician. Some sites even offer physician consultations without revealing the doctor's name, address, or qualifications. These online visits can be even more costly than the average office visit, without the benefit of a physical examination.

My advice is to look for sites that are reputable and are linked to leading universities or research centers. Research the credentials and affiliations of individual physicians who have websites. Remember – recommendations tend to be generalized and may not apply to your specific situation.

It is true that the more informed you are, the greater your ability to take charge of your health. It's okay to look for information on the web, but most people do not have the appropriate training and experience to determine the best course of action when a problem arises. My recommendation is that you should enter into a relationship with a health-care provider whom you feel you can trust, ask any questions, and know that your needs are being addressed – where you are allowed to take part in the decision-making process concerning your health and well-being.

A woman needs to develop a trusting relationship in order to work with her health-care provider. If she doesn't have a satisfactory relationship with her provider, she should consider finding someone with whom she feels confident. Personally, I have complete faith in my gynecologist, my mechanic, and Karen my editor. When I need assistance with my health, auto, or writing my books, I follow *their* advice.

Healthier lifestyles, medical advances and preventive choices mean that we will live longer and healthier than our ancestors. Today, a positive approach to life and longevity includes taking responsibility for every facet of your life, especially your wonderful body.

Please check my website at **www.drcarolle.com** for updated information and research.

Let's stay well together!

REFERENCES

Greenlee RT, Hill-Harmon, MD, Murray T, Thun M. Cancer statistics, 2001. *CA Cancer J Clin.* 2001;51:15-36.

Stitik FP, Tockman MD, Frost JK, et al. Lung cancer mortality in males screened by chest x-ray and cytologic sputum examination: a preliminary report. Recent Results Cancer Res. 1982;83:138-146.

Melamed MR, Flehinger BJ, Zaman MB, Heelan RT, Perchick WA, Martini N. Screening for early lung cancer. Results of the Memorial Sloan-Kettering Study in New York. *Chest.* 1984;86:44-53.

American Cancer Society: *Cancer Facts and Figures 2000.*

Miller AB, Baines CJ, To T, et al. Canadian national Breast Screening Study: 1. Breast cancer detection and death rates among women aged 50 to 59. CMAJ. 1992;147:1459-1476.

Kewenter J, Bjork S, Haglind E, Smith L, Svanvik J, Ahren C. Screening and rescreening for colorectal cancer: a controlled trial of fecal occult blood testing in 27,000 subjects. *Cancer.* 1988;62:645-651.

The Henry J. Kaiser Family Foundation. Emergency contraception. *Kaiser Family Foundation Fact Sheet.* November 2000.

American College of Obstetricians and Gynecologist. The pill at 40: woman say it's safer, has extra benefits but not covered by insurance. *ACOG News Release*; May 2, 2000.

Deep 6 for N-9 clears way for other microbicide trials. *STD Advisor* 2000;3:73-75,80.

Trussell J, Card JJ, Rowland Hogue CJ. Adolescent sexual behavior, pregnancy and childbearing. Hatcher, et al. *Contraceptive Technology.* 17th Revised Edition, (New York): (Ardent Media, Inc.);1998:701-744.

Blumel JE, Castelo-Branco C, Rocangliolo ME, Bifa L, Tacla X, Mamani L *Menopause.* 2001;8:239-244

Section Three

SOUL

YOUR SPIRITUAL HEALTH

Your Spiritual Health

He who loses money, loses much;
He who loses a friend, loses much more;
He who loses faith, loses all.

What is our "soul" and how does it relate to our health? Deep inside, we all *know* we have a spiritual dimension. If we become aware, we acknowledge that soul, spirit, religion and/or spirituality are all different words for the same concept of a power greater than our individual egos. I have a personal story to tell you about how difficult it was to find spiritual health, which is one of the four equally important aspects of a balanced life. Sometimes ego, even a doctor's, is forced to recognize that there is more to life than meets the eye...

I had a frightening panic attack in New York in June of 2000 that became a catalyst for my own personal spiritual healing. But it was not an easy path. Adapting my usual "wanting to be in control" attitude, I researched and read about the subject, and then carefully followed recommendations suggested by Dr. Bourne in his book *The Anxiety & Phobia Workbook.* I dutifully saw my therapist, Denise, and did healing-touch sessions with Robert Leak. This was only the beginning of what turned out to be a long journey of discovery – and I was never again the same person I had been.

The old me believed in the power of my will and my mind, and that going to church didn't make you any more spiritual than going to a garage made you a mechanic. Many things in my background had made me turn my back on "religion," and I'd had more than a few thoughts about how all the various and conflicting concepts of God were probably man-made.

But Dr. Bourne wrote about the significance of *developing* one's spirituality, and his words penetrated through my ego and my "thinking system." He said, "Spirituality involves the recognition and acceptance of a Higher Power, beyond your own intelligence and will, with whom you can have a relationship. This Higher Power can provide you with inspiration, joy, security, peace of mind, and guidance, far exceeding what is possible in the absence of the belief in a Higher Power."

He further writes, "spiritual awareness and growth can effect a transformation in your whole being. It can help you develop a basic trust and faith, which is unshakable." Further, "as you develop your spirituality, many of your beliefs about the meaning of life in general, and what your life is about specifically, can shift dramatically. These shifts in beliefs can lead to having more compassion and tolerance toward yourself, as well as to finding a deeper meaning in the challenges you face, instead of viewing them as arbitrary and meaningless. You may feel less like a victim who has a particular problem with anxiety. Instead, you may come to regard your condition as an *opportunity* to grow and expand who you are."

This advice made sense to me and started me on a path of changing my attitude toward spirituality.

☖

Scientific Research on Spirituality and Health

According to the results of a recent 28-year study of 5,000 churchgoers, those who regularly attended religious services lived longer than those who did not. Non-churchgoers experienced a 36% higher death rate as compared to churchgoers. It was theorized that this discrepancy could be explained by increased social contacts, improved health practices, more stable marriages, and perhaps, the belief in, and practice of, prayer.

According to a 1995 study at Dartmouth's Hitchcock Medical Center, one of the strongest predictors of survival after open-heart surgery was the degree to which patients said they drew strength and comfort from religion. Patients comforted by their faith were three times more likely to be alive six months after open-heart surgery than patients who found no comfort in religion.

The current medical establishment is beginning to embrace spirituality. In the early 1990's only a few medical schools taught spirituality. Today, spirituality is taught at about 50 of the 125 medical schools in the US This demand is the result of students who see that there is more to technology when it comes to health. One of the courses, "Religious Traditions in Health Care," seeks to understand the major world religions from a medical perspective, and the correlation between spirituality and health. And spiritual history is now included in medical history courses.

In *The Open Heart Secret of Happiness,* Lester Savage wrote: "Medical science now recognizes that the body and the spirit interact, and that a happy spirit can help heal the body and then assist in keeping it healthy."

Psychiatrist Martin W. Jones of Howard University College of Medicine, studies the correlation between faith and healing. He points out that it is not at all important to have a complete explanation or understanding of the effect of spirituality on our health.

Spiritual Growth in Times of Trouble

Spirituality seems to increase greatly during times of hardship. Since the terrorist attacks on September 11, 2001, many individuals have sought to connect more deeply with their spirituality. Church attendance almost doubled at some houses of worship, and attendance remained high months later. Initially, people needed a place to make their prayers official, to connect with their community. The antidote to chaos is faith.

When things are "normal," it is typical for people to rush around, taking care of jobs, responsibilities and everyone around them, and forgetting to take the time to nourish their own spirituality. For some of these individuals, this pattern may continue until tragedy strikes, rending a sense of loss, mortality, and vulnerability. They find themselves lost, unable to cope, unsure where to turn for help. Sometimes these individuals return to their church, to their lost spirituality, to put them back on course. I have known many women my own age, accomplished in all they desired, ending up lost, attempting to figure out who they are as people. At this point, all the material trappings of success are meaningless. The shock of having panic attacks was my own personal wake-up call on this subject.

My "Spiritual History"

It has been my experience that religion tends to connect us to our spirituality through dogma and practice. Growing up in Haiti, I did not have good experiences with religion and, further, equated religion with spirituality. I suffered greatly as a child because of religious beliefs surrounding me.

My dear grandfather, Mirabeau, was a highly-respected voodoo priest in the region where I lived. However, I attended parochial school. At the age of 9, the nuns learned about my grandfather and I was thrown out of school. I was told that my grandfather was an evil man. The church condemned a relative I adored, a good and caring man who healed the sick, and inspired me to be a healer. I was tormented and could only handle this terrible conflict by turning my back on the church.

As I grew up, more conflicts confronted me about religion in Haitian history. It made no sense to me that one could commit many crimes and still be entitled to go to heaven if one simply repent before taking their last breath. I questioned the very existence of a God. I never realized that organized religion had nothing to do with the existence of God. I abhorred the self-righteous advocates of a church that claimed only they would be saved because others do not know and follow the "real" truth – their truth. Whose truth? Are the Gods of Islam, Judaism, Christianity and all the other belief systems one and the same God?

Rudy Giuliani, former mayor of New York City, eloquently stated: "Whether we are in a mosque, church or synagogue, we are talking to God in every language that he understands. We are using hymns and liturgy, and I know we are getting through to the same God." *But who was my God?*

Prayers and Health

Many people find answers to life's tragedies in prayer. Studies have documented lower rates of depression and anxiety-related illness among those who pray. Other studies have demonstrated better outcomes among patients who were prayed for, as compared to patients who were not.

When my brother-in-law, Guy, was very badly burned in an auto accident in Florida, he was not expected to live. His rescue was caught on video and aired on television for days after the accident. As he battled for his life, all of Miami prayed for him. Everyone believed that it was a miracle that he survived. It was even more powerful that he accepted it all. One day, Julienne, a family friend and nurse at Jackson Memorial Hospital, told me the following story.

Whenever she could, Julienne sat at Guy's bedside and prayed for him. She reminded Guy of his faith, and told him that he would make it. She encouraged him to accept unconditionally any physical limitations placed on him, that his will to live was stronger than his pain and fear, and that he would be grateful to live. At first, there was no response. Then she could tell that he was listening, and he would squeeze her finger once for yes and twice for no. Julienne never wavered in her belief that Guy would make it and be okay. He is. His body is scarred, but not his beautiful spirit.

Growing up in Haiti and living through many heart-wrenching medical situations, I believed that I survived and helped others heal with prayer, even though I was not following any dogmatic religion. *As a healer I believed in prayer for others, but not for myself.* I have prayed for patients undergoing chemotherapy or life-threatening surgeries. I always ask the date and exact time the surgery will take place, and I pray during those times. While working in obstetrics, my Grandma and I prayed whenever a premature baby was in neonatal intensive care. Prayer was always one of my tools, but strangely enough, I did not apply it to myself.

On the Search for Spirituality

"Baby Boomers" (born between 1946 and 1964) have been known to reject organized religion, but, as they age, this trend seems to be reversing. Baby boomers are turning to spirituality, but not necessarily in the form of organized religion. Interest is increasing in a variety of expressions of spirituality: Buddhism, Hinduism, Native American teachings, ancient goddess traditions, and other "New Age" belief systems. Many of the baby boomers have achieved great financial successes, but find that something still is lacking. For many of them, religion or spirituality may fill this void. (I had an "a-void" going on.)

In spite of my ongoing therapy for anxiety, I remained uncomfortable in enclosed spaces. I lacked the courage to attend a dear friend's 50th birthday party because it was being held on a boat. My wake up call was knocking again. Others had counseled me that prayer would help, but where and how to begin? Faith does not appear automatically on demand. So I started seeking.

I attended a Christian church twice with a friend. I tried chanting with another friend who studied the Eckenkart religion – a religion based on the light and sound of God. I meditated, I read spiritual books and articles. Perhaps, if I were in Haiti, I would have attended a ceremony at my grandfather's voodoo temple. Nothing seemed to work. I was now ready to walk naked, on my head, down the middle of the freeway. Or, maybe medication was the answer, even with unwanted side effects? No, there must be a better answer for me.

At the funeral of my friend Charlotte's husband, it seemed as if the preacher was talking directly to me. He spoke about faith. "Faith," he said, "does not come on command. Just ask God, or Jesus, to ease your heart and wait." Was he asking for patience from me? – a headstrong, black woman doctor? I floundered for inspiration, but not for long.

The miracle of my bother-in-law Guy's survival inspired and encouraged me. While he still required more surgeries and rehabilitation for disfiguring burn injuries, Guy remained strong for his wife, Elsie, as she battled breast cancer. He was not only strong for her, he remained strong for all of us. He comforted *us* and gave each of us strength, in spite of his personal tragedies. I realized then that this was why his life had been spared, to be a spiritual pillar for our family. Once, I told Guy that I wished that I had his strength and faith. He told me it was not merely strength and faith – he said "you have to let go." I was still troubled about what this meant and reflected on other examples in my life…

I have a friend, Alama, who lives in Sierra Leone, in spite of their civil war. I worried about her safety. Her brother, Henry, told me of neighbors murdered by the rebels. Once, I asked Alama why she did not move to the US, where she and her husband would be safe. She told me that Sierra Leone was her country, her home, and she wanted to stay there until she died. She was unafraid because she prayed, and that her faith was strong. She believed that she would die when it was her time, regardless of where she lived.

My sister, Marise, experienced a period of great stress in her life. She told me that her faith in God kept her going. She spoke of the "faith of the mustard seed" from the Book of Promises, where a sick person can claim their healing and believe that they are already healed.

My therapist suggested that I should ask my Grandma for guidance. But, how could I? Grandma had already passed away. I decided to use Grandma's olivewood rosary to help me feel close to her. This rosary was very special as a remembrance of my Grandma, but it didn't have a religious significance to me. The story of how she got it is interesting…

My Grandma had once prayed for a patient of mine who wanted to have a baby but was unsuccessful after years of effort. A month after my Grandma's prayer, the couple got pregnant. The husband was to travel to Israel and asked what he could bring my Grandma in appreciation for her prayers. Her only wish was to own a rosary made of olivewood from the Mount of Olives in Israel. He found a beautiful, hand-carved olivewood rosary and purchased it for her, although he certainly received many surprised looks. Not many Jewish men purchase rosaries.

Grandma loved her rosary. After she passed away, we realized with horror that we did not place the rosary – as per our custom – in her hands before we buried her. I guess the rosary was not supposed to be buried as it still had a mission to accomplish: to help me, Grandma's favorite granddaughter.

I sat on my bed with the rosary in my hands and cried. I set it aside and read through her prayer book. I could see her seated in her favorite chair, in our backyard in Haiti, reading from this book. "Grandma, I do not like the way I am feeling, please come to help me," I begged. I saw her smiling at me. What did she say as she endured tough times? When there was not enough food to feed us? When my father had financial and political troubles and our shoes were worn out? The answer came to me then: "Que ta volonte sois faite." *"Thy will be done."*

I went to sleep that night repeating "Que ta volonte sois faite." I chanted this over and over and clutched her rosary. The more I repeated "Que ta volonte sois faite," the stronger I felt. When I awoke, it was morning and the sun was high in the sky. I felt rested and realized I wasn't experiencing any more fears. A spiritual healing had occurred that night for me – a miracle, if you will. *I had asked for help and woke up no longer worried about being in control.*

A quantum leap. I had finally let go of having to be in charge and be in control. My ego versus a bigger power. I was tested, as many traumas followed, but I was not shattered. My sister Elsie required many additional surgeries due to her breast cancer. Marise's husband was involved in a severe auto accident and injured his spine. For a while we thought he would end up a quadriplegic. But for the first time, I was able to let go and let God take over.

Each time I visit Haiti, my homeland, I return feeling stronger. There I watch my people living in extreme poverty, working in harsh environments. But, Haitians are always hopeful that tomorrow will be a better day – that God will provide for them. They live simple lives. "Bon Dieu Bon" – "Good is good," they say with great hope even during times when their most basic needs are unmet. They are grateful for the small things; they thank God for what they have and do not complain about things they do not have. It is indeed the truth that money is not the answer to happiness.

Today, I sometimes attend church, and I pray from time to time, when I feel like it. My husband, Albert, and I often pray together on Sunday. With my prayers comes more strength and joy. But there are many other things that I do that help me to continue to grow spiritually. I'd like to share them with you.

🌱🌱🌱

About Sorrow

"Sorrow looks back,
worry looks around,
and faith looks up!"

A W. Tozer wrote, "God can't use a person to the maximum until he or she has been hurt deeply." I recently read an article by Professor Abdulaziz Sachedina, of the Department of Religious Studies at the University of Virginia, in which he commented on the circumstances of September 11, 2001. He had found a poem, written by Jalaluddin Rumi, which spoke to his pain.

"Sorrow prepares you for joy. It violently sweeps everything out of your house, so that new joy can find space to enter. It shakes the yellow leaves from the bough of your heart, so that fresh, green leaves can grow in their place. It pulls up the rotten roots, so that new roots hidden beneath have room to grow. Whatever sorrow shakes from your heart, far better things will have their place."

I see now that my wake up call experiences with anxiety and panic were opportunities to grow spiritually. I am now a much stronger person. This newfound strength benefits not only myself, but also all those around me. We can put sorrow and personal pain to work. Even realizing our own mortality can be life–empowering

On Being Nurtured by Nature

When we experience worry, grief, sorrow, or uncertainty, our focus tends to narrow. Taking some time to look around us and enjoy nature can help us to heal.

One of my examination room windows overlooks a San Diego freeway. Just above the retaining wall is a large area planted thickly with iceplant. About twice a year, this usually green area suddenly changes into a bed of pink blossoms. I had always marveled at the beauty of small flowers. But, as a sort of accidental miracle for me, nested among the little pink flowers is an area full of purple blossoms. For some unknown reason, the purple patch has a soothing effect upon my soul. Through the years, whenever I felt exhausted, or tired of the rat race, I would be rejuvenated if I could look at the flowers. Sometimes I regret they do not bloom more often, but I am grateful to enjoy this serendipity of nature for several weeks.

Deborah and Susan, mother and daughter, have been my patients for many years. One day Deborah told me that her 32-year-old daughter Susan had died. I was shocked. I had always heard that losing a child is one of the most painful experiences a parent could endure. What could I say to Deborah? How to console her? When I told her that I was sorry to hear about Susan, she smiled faintly. "Do not worry about me," she said. "I am doing pretty well, I think. Life must go on. I have to be strong for my family, especially for my grandchildren."

"How do you do it?" I asked her. "How do you find the strength to go on?"

"I take it day by day." Deborah added, "One day at a time. I do feel sad from time to time. Sometimes I lay awake all night, unable to sleep. And when I fall asleep, I may just have nightmares. But when I awake, I am thankful to God that he is giving me a chance to see another day, that I am alive, that my health is still good. Sometimes, you know, we are too busy in life to appreciate the little things. I have been taking my time and enjoying every little thing since Susan died."

"Look, look," she continued. "Look at those beautiful pink flowers across the freeway. I was admiring them while waiting for you. And, look at that little patch of purple flowers. Isn't it beautiful? You see, Dr. Carolle, those are the little things that keep me going."

Deborah did not have to explain any more. I knew about the insignificant things we sometimes pass by without noticing. Those little things are indeed what uplifts us if we take the time to stop, see, and be grateful.

After having my panic attack, I learned that spending time in my garden was one of the best things I could do for myself. I was lucky to have a house with a half-acre of flat land that could be transformed into a garden. I soon learned how expensive small plants were, and was grateful that my friends (Laurie, Linda, Edna, Shirley and Lois) were willing to share plants from their own gardens. My garden gives me a connection to nature and a beautiful balance with work.

> *One day, while working in the garden, I witnessed something wonderful. A dozen small birds were playing a game. Each bird stood on the ground, about a foot away from the next one. Close to my fence is a 12-foot hedge, and one by one, each bird flew straight into this hedge, hitting it head-on. Some birds reached the top, some only the middle. They lost themselves within the foliage, screaming and screeching. When they grew tired, they flew back to the ground. Then, the routine began again. The creatures of nature can remind our spirits to play.*

Since 1999, I have made many trips to my native country of Haiti, along with a team of volunteers. We provide free medical care and coordinate projects for the children. I returned to Haiti after experiencing my panic attacks, and was engulfed with numerous feelings too difficult to describe Somehow, this trip contributed to my healing, and it was as if setting foot on my native soil allowed me to be reborn. A rejuvenating potion had been instilled in my veins.

La Vallee de Jacmel is a small town nestled in a chain of mountains, overlooking the Caribbean Sea, in the southeastern part of Haiti. There is something magical about the sky, the clouds, the gentle winds, and the calm sea far away.

During my visits, I spend long hours at the hospital, and with the children. In the evenings, I meet with village leaders to prioritize the few resources we bring to share. One night, I went to bed around midnight, wondering if I would have the strength to accomplish all I had scheduled the next day. I awoke after only a few hours of sleep. I went to my balcony, overlooking a cliff. While everyone else slept, I sat and communed with nature. No lights disturbed the night, as the generator only operates between 6 and 9 in the evening. As my eyes adjusted to the light, I saw stars all around me, millions of them. It felt as if I could just reach up and touch them.

I remembered the days of my childhood, so full of dreams that I wished they could all come true. Overwhelmed by my tiredness, and the beauty that surrounded me, I began to cry. The tears were about my own suffering, my pain, the living conditions that surrounded me, and thoughts of the demanding day ahead. But my soul was fed by the joy of being able to witness this beauty.

I returned to bed and fell deeply asleep. A familiar noise awakened me with a start. It was a rooster, melodiously welcoming me to the morning. Other roosters joined in, and soon it was an orchestra. I ran to the balcony and saw the most beautiful vision. There was no sign yet of the sun. Little by little, the dark blue sky brightened, until the sun appeared majestically at the horizon. The coconut and fruit trees could no longer hide. The donkeys joined the rooster's orchestra. The brighter the day became, the stronger I felt nurtured by nature.

On Being Grateful

Being grateful exercises your soul. A wonderful thing Denise, my therapist, taught me was to create a "Grateful List." You simply write down what you are grateful for. When you find yourself in times of doubt or sadness, pick up and read your "Grateful List." You are less prone to be unhappy when you focus on things you are grateful for. You are more likely to be optimistic and feel good about yourself, and share your blessings.

So, please sit down and make a list of the things you are grateful for, and add to it whenever you can. Here is my list, as an example.

I am grateful for:

- Enjoying all the different kind of work that I do
- Being healthy
- Having a loving husband, and having…
- Good friends
- My relatives
- My devoted patients
- My Grandma, who came into my life to teach me beautiful lessons
- Those who support my foundation and make it possible to help the children of Haiti
- Being tolerant
- Being optimistic and finding the best in everything and everyone
- Being able to judge all beings by their character, and not their skin color, their material possessions, or their religion
- Having been given many opportunities in my lifetime and being able to take advantage of them
- Recognition of what I have to share with others

- Knowing that it is imperative to strive to make this world a better place
- That special look in the eyes of a mother in La Vallee whose daughter I helped to heal with my skills
- For the wonderful feeling that engulfs me after returning from a medical mission in Haiti or from the clinic here in San Diego
- That I have skills that enable me to help others, diagnose and provide treatment
- Being okay with my reflection in the mirror
- Knowing that I have learned to take life one day at a time
- Cutting roses and irises from my garden to place in my kitchen
- Feeling happy watching birds fly and play in my backyard
- Watching a fox in my backyard and realizing that I am experiencing a rare visit
- Having a good gardener (good, dependable gardeners are hard to find in my area)
- Discovering a beautiful tree I had previously missed and pausing to say, "hello friend"
- Recognizing my fortune to live in America
- Being grateful to be alive
- Being able to leave the world a better place when I am gone
- Just being alone sometimes.

About Giving

"It is more blessed to give than to receive".

The bible is full of passages related to giving and recommendations that one tithe, or give, their church 10% of their earnings. I believe the art of giving is a state of mind and has nothing to do with one's wealth. People who seem to give the most are typically less rich when it comes to counting material possessions and money, but are wealthy in many other ways.

I read somewhere that the wealthiest person is the one who needs the least. My Grandma was the wealthiest person I have ever met. When she died, she had less than $500 in her bank account. But, she could have had anything she wanted because her children and grandchildren loved her and learned from her giving nature. I remember buying her a beautiful rocking chair for her 80th birthday. She thanked me and said, "Please do not buy me any more things. If you really want to give me something, give me money to send to my poor friends in Haiti."

My early lessons about giving and sharing were from Grandma. Growing up, we did not have a lot, but somehow she always managed to put aside something for the church and for the poor. "You give because you have to, not because you want people to know how nice you are," was her philosophy. "The right hand should never know what the left hand is doing when it comes to giving. There is no more powerful instance than to know that with your help you can change the life of so many. Giving should be from the heart."

> *I will never forget one time that Grandma and I visited the open market. I was about nine years old and I was talking about all the things I wanted Grandma to buy for me. She told me that money was scarce. My father worked for the government and sometimes as many as three months passed between his paychecks. My Grandma worked very hard to make ends meet. That day she only had five dollars to spend at the market, not enough to buy the barest of necessities.*
>
> *On the way to the market, a very distraught woman stopped us and begged us to give her some change. One of her children was very sick and she could not afford to buy the medications that she needed. Without hesitation, Grandma gave the woman a dollar. She and I had just been talking about being short of money. There were so many things we could have gotten with that dollar. Although Grandma knew that sometimes people lied about a child being sick to get money from people, she said that we had to give anyway, because one could never know the truth and the woman may really need the money to care for a sick child.*

Grandma taught me that it is not necessary to know a person before you help them. Do not give merely to hear, "Oh, what a nice person you are." You give because you want to give, never expecting anything in return. She told me about the Albert Schweitzer Hospital in Haiti. The sick walked many miles to receive care and it was always given to them. I learned it is not how much you have, but how much you have to share with others that matters.

After Grandma's advice, I have heard many *conflicting* ideas about abundance and giving from people throughout my life: "You have to be careful how much you give and to whom you give." "Charity begins at home." "Give to a good charity of your choice." "God helps those who help themselves." "Give to family and friends and those who are really in need, not to those who wish to take advantage of you." "If someone is in need, do not offer a loan but instead give as much as you can afford – a loan is only a burden to the one in need."

We live in a world of abundance and many of us have more than we need. I believe if we understand this and share what we have with others, we will never want for anything. Louise Hay said it eloquently:

"The more I give, the more I have."

Wealth is more than money; and so there is much that we can give others *besides* money. Sometimes a small gift of time or energy at the right time can make a world of difference. I remember telling my friend, Sheri, about the lack of electricity at the Hospital in La Vallee, Haiti. When performing a Pap smear at that hospital, I would have to ask someone to hold a flashlight so I could see. This was very humiliating for me, and the patient. The day before I left for Haiti, Sheri called to say that she had a special gift for the women of La Vallee. Her husband Bob had designed and constructed a special adjustable headlamp that could be switched on and off during pelvic exams. What a blessed gift!

The Power of Music

I know there is something spiritual about music. Henry Wadsworth Longfellow wrote:

"God sent His singers upon earth
With songs of gladness and of mirth
That they might touch the hearts of men,
And bring them back to heaven again."

One summer evening I was listening to the San Diego Symphony orchestra at the Embarcadero open-air theater. The sky was full of stars. On each table was a small vase with a candle. The Romeros, a family of four generations of classical guitar players, also entertained that night. When they played one of my favorites, "Aranjuez," the music went straight to my heart, enveloping me from head to toe. If there is a heaven on earth, this is it! I thought to myself. When it was over, I felt like screaming. Then, the unexpected occurred. One person in the audience started to scream, then two, then ten, and soon all of us were screaming. The music awakened something so powerful within the people in that audience that "Bravo" would not have sufficed. I screamed for what felt like an eternity.

Not only can music move your soul and be inspirational – there are scientific experiments that prove the vibrations of different music affects the growth of plants. Why not humans too?

There are many songs that make me feel closer to God, but none like "Ave Maria," or when Charles Aznavour (the French equivalent of Frank Sinatra) sings "Merci mon Dieu:"

"Thank-you God.
My heart was lost until you showed me the way.
A path full of hope that fills empty dreams with desire to live.
Thank-you God.
What I was hoping to achieve on this earth
And that I prayed for
You made it happen.
Since I found love and happiness
I want to say with all my heart
Thank-you God."

Praying Together

I am part of an Internet prayer group of Haitians from all over the world. We pray for peace in the world, and especially for Haiti. This group is lead by my friend Monique Theodore. Every Friday, we receive a prayer. This one below touched my soul. It is a prayer by Francis of Assisi. We live in a chaotic world where there is so much suffering. If we could all live by these words, the world would be a better place:

> *Lord, make me an instrument of your peace.*
> *Where there is hatred, let me sow love.*
> *Where there is injury, pardon.*
> *Where there is doubt, faith.*
> *Where there is despair, hope.*
> *Where there is darkness, light.*
> *And where there is sadness, joy.*
>
> *O Divine Master,*
> *Grant me that I may not so much seek*
> *To be consoled as to console,*
> *To be understood as to understand,*
> *To be loved as to love.*
> *For it is in giving that we receive.*
> *It is in pardoning that we are pardoned,*
> *And in dying that we are born into eternal life.*

Learn How to Be Forgiving

"Forgiveness is freeing – for yourself as well as for others. It frees you from carrying the burden of past resentments. It allows you to release the past so that all your energy can be fully available for the present. Forgiveness is the ultimate gift you can give yourself."
—Author unknown

I have noticed that many of my patients who were abused physically, mentally, or sexually, carry that burden throughout their lives. This burden may stop them from having healthy relationships with their children, peers, and intimate partners. I learned first-hand that in order to be free, a victim has to learn to forgive, or else they will continue to be a victim for the rest of their life.

My mother was too poor to raise me in her little village in Haiti. I was four years old and my sister, Marise, was two when my distraught mother took us to live with Grandma. After my father left my mother, he refused to support my mother financially unless we went to live with his mother, Tatante. Tatante was adamant that Marise and I were raised without contact with my mother's family. She was strict and disrespectful to my mother. I felt like I didn't belong anywhere. I resented Tatante for being mean to us, and for how she treated my mother and her family.

Logically, I understood that the way things worked out, I had received a better education, being the first in my mother's family to graduate from high school. I loved my father, but could not forgive him for abandoning my mother. Unconsciously, I had never forgiven my mother for abandoning us as little children. I did not comprehend the heavy burden I carried, but it became clear many years later while working with my therapist.

I did not realize the importance of forgiveness until I had the panic attack. I learned that one way to avoid panic attacks was *to forgive*. I needed to forgive anyone that I felt had hurt me. I have often read that one has to learn to forgive, that letting go will make one a happier and healthier person. But, like many people, I found that hard to do.

According to scientists, a lot of anger and hostility are present in our society due to unresolved conflicts. This results in a high incidence of domestic abuse, drug and alcohol abuse, violence, divorce, and even crime. We have seen teenagers from middle class families go on killing sprees in their schools as the result of unresolved conflicts and anger.

Studies have documented the psychological benefits of forgiveness: reduced anxiety, stress, and depression. Individuals who harbor anger increase their risk of heart attack, and decrease the response capacity of their immune systems. Once you forgive, anger is decreased, you feel better about yourself, and personal relationships are enhanced.

Forgiveness can be defined as "recognizing you have been wronged, giving up all resulting resentment, and eventually responding to the offending person with compassion and even love." Forgiving does not mean that you deny that you have been wronged, nor is it condoning or excusing your abuse. The key to true forgiveness is letting go of the anger and negative feelings associated with the person or situation.

When I started having the panic attacks, I was willing to do anything to make them go away. I decided to try something I had read about. The idea is to indirectly confront the person you wish to forgive by writing down everything about how a specific person has wronged you. I used this process to forgive Tatante, who was alive and living in Miami, and my mother who was already dead.

How the "forgiving exercise" works:
1. First write down everything you feel that the person has done wrong to you. Get it all out – be as specific as possible.

    Dear Tatante,
    You hurt me every time you say something bad about my mother. You hurt me when you refused to let me see my mother or her relatives. You hurt me every time you criticized me, whether or not I had done right or wrong, or just did not meet your standards.

    Dear Mom,
    You never should have let Marise and I stay with Tatante. You should have fought for us, rescued us, even though it would have meant that we would not have gotten as good an education.

2. Now practice telling the person everything that you want him or her to know. If the hurt was done when you were a child, then the confident grown-up you – who is not afraid of that person – takes the shy, scared child onto your lap and has the child tell it all.

When it was time to read my list to Tatante, I realized that the hurt started when I was four years old. I held Ti-Ca – my nickname as a little girl – on my lap and had Ti-Ca read the list to Tatante.

Since I became conscious of the resentment I had towards my mother as an adult, I saw myself seated in her living room, as an adult, talking to her face to face.

3. Write down positive things that the person who hurt you has done for you. If there are none, that's okay. If you keep thinking, you may remember something kind that this person has done for you.

    I was surprised to realize that Tatante had done many positive things for me. For many years, we stayed at her house. When my father could not afford it, she would feed us, pay our tuition, pay for uniforms, books, tutors, and the endless things we needed for school.

    Regarding my mother, I can only remember her look of hopelessness when I visited her. Because of that look, I decided I would never put myself in her situation. This gave me the courage to overcome many obstacles, to become successful, independent, and well educated, so I would never have to make similar sacrifices.

4. Lastly, practice telling the person that you forgive him or her, because they did not know any better.

    "Tatante," "Maman," I said, "I forgive you since you did not know any better."

By the time I got to this part. I was sobbing. I cried for awhile, letting the tears clean my soul. This was the first time I ever really shed tears for my mother, since she died almost a year earlier. When I was done crying, I felt a huge weight had been lifted from my heart and my brain.

The next time I went to Florida to visit Marise and Tatante, we had a great time together. I saw Tatante one more time, six months later during a stopover on the way to Haiti. She prepared my favorite meal and helped me rearrange my luggage. I told her that I loved her and I really meant it. Three weeks later, she became gravely ill and passed away. I went back for her funeral. At the wake, I looked at her lying motionless in her coffin. There was no more hurt, no more hate, just love and gratitude. Tatante never understood why I resented her. She felt that she had done her best. Forgiving her not only gave me a chance to heal myself, it gave her the opportunity to enjoy the company of a niece she loved and for whom she had made many sacrifices.

Isn't it time for you to forgive someone?

Concluding Thoughts on Spirituality

"Yesterday is history, tomorrow is mystery, today is a gift."

It's a challenge to be, and remain, aware of our divine source. To balance our lives, I believe we all must learn how to create a personal world in which we remember the spiritual aspect of life.

Being part of the computer age, I received the following list by email on how to remain spiritual in the new millennium, supposedly written by the Dalai Lama. It's an inspired list, whoever wrote it!

1. Take into account that great love and great achievements involve great risk.
2. When you lose, don't lose the lesson.
3. Follow the three Rs: Respect for self, respect for others, Responsibility for all your actions.
4. Remember that not getting what you want is sometimes a wonderful stroke of luck.
5. Learn the rules so you know how to break them properly.
6. Don't let a little dispute injure a great friendship.
7. When you realize you've made a mistake, take immediate steps to correct it.

8. Spend some time alone every day.
9. Open your arms to change, but don't let go of your values.
10. Remember that silence is sometimes the best answer.
11. Live a good, honorable life. Then when you get older and think back, you'll be able to enjoy it a second time.
12. A loving atmosphere in your home is the foundation for your life.
13. In disagreements with loved ones, deal only with the current situation.
14. Share your knowledge. It's a way to achieve immortality.
15. Be gentle with the earth.Once a year, go someplace you've never been before.
16. Remember that the best relationship is one in which your love for each other exceeds your need for each other.
17. Judge your success by what you had to give up in order to get it.
18. Approach love and cooking with reckless abandon.

🌱🌱

To me, admitting you have a soul and then taking care of it means spiritual health. How do you take care of it? *Find whatever you call a higher power and lay your ego at its feet.* Doing this will free your soul to have faith and trust in something bigger than yourself. It will give you a broader perspective on life and the lessons we are here to learn.

Be grateful for everything that happens to you, negative *and* positive because these experiences are your teachers. This planet is a huge schoolroom – anything that happens can be transformed into something positive by your spiritual beliefs, thoughts and deeds.

Having faith, as well as practicing forgiveness, giving from your heart, and having a connection with nature will lighten your stress, your sorrows, and your heart.

🌱🌱

Section Four

MONEY

YOUR
FINANCIAL
HEALTH

Your Financial Health

When some people heard I was writing a book about health *and money,* they wondered why, as these topics are not typically connected. I explained that our *financial health* is directly connected to our *overall health.* Remember my panic attacks? My body and soul needed to heal, and I needed to take a step back to re-evaluate my career, which took a while. Taking that time out was possible only because I had savings and knew how to live frugally.

The intent of this chapter is to debunk the many misconceptions about our relationship with money, not to teach you expert financial planning – I'm not a financial planner. But with considerable experiences with patients in my private practice, patients at homeless shelters, friends, and relatives, I feel compelled to include the influence of money on our health. It is one of those four important "legs": mind, body, soul and money. We must control our financial health in order for our "table" of optimum health not to wobble.

THE MONEY-HEALTH CONNECTION

Much of life revolves around money: earning money, learning how to spend money, saving and giving. *I have learned that how one feels about money has nothing to do with how much you have.* And how much money we make has nothing to do with how much we save. America is one of the few countries where anyone who works hard and has the ability to save can become the millionaire next door. We hear the stories of people who win millions of dollars from the lottery – promptly spend or lose it all. And there are the once-rich and successful celebrities who end up in bankruptcy due to poor money management.

Our relationship with money is twofold: *earning it and spending it.* Earnings are related to our educational capacity as well as our lifestyle needs. When our earnings exceed our basic costs of living, we are able to save. How much we are paid for what we do varies in many ways. Where we live, our skills, gender, ethnicity, and job availability all enter the equation. Doctors in Russia and Cuba earn about the same as other professionals. Almost everywhere movie stars and athletes earn more than most. The ballplayer earns far more than the teacher who teaches our children.

Our environment also reflects our relationship with money. My paternal grandmother raised me because my single mother was poor. Although Grandma also struggled, she taught me invaluable lessons about frugality. She was adamant that "we do not eat the turkey today and the feathers tomorrow." We learned to live with each day's allotment. She taught us the difference between "needs and wants." *Needs* are things we must have to live decently, such as a secure home, food, and money for basic necessities. Everything else should be considered *wants.*

Americans are driven by consumerism; teenagers want to have it all and have it *now.* They do not realize that money affords independence and security, and is not merely the means to acquire new things. Children spend too much time watching television and being lured by prizes inside happy meals. Many teenagers who grow up during times of prosperity learn to have a materialistic attitude. They are bombarded by MTV images, where clothes define a person. Peer pressure drives teens to want the latest fashions, proms cost thousands of dollars, and they believe they need their own telephone lines, cellular phones, computers, CD players, and on and on. Money and what it buys helps them to feel they fit in.

According to WonderGroup, an agency that conducts in-depth research for corporations, about two-thirds of children live in single-parent households or have two parents who work outside the home. To compensate for the lack of attention, parents buy more things for their children out of guilt. As a result, some children may learn to equate money with love. According to Teenage Research Unlimited, a market research firm, teen-agers spend an average of $84 per week – $27 from their parents and $57 from a job or other source, shelling out a staggering $155 billion in the year 2000. Additionally, they rack up thousands of dollars in credit card debt.

Parents who live beyond their means, amassing huge debt, often influence their children's relationships with money. Marvin Goldberg, a business professor at Pennsylvania State University, found that when parents stated, "I'd rather spend time shopping than doing almost anything else," their children were likely to learn accordingly: "The more money you have, the happier you are."

THE HEALTH IMPACT OF FINANCIAL PROBLEMS

Researchers from Ontario York University studied the negative impact of unstable income on health. Their results suggested that sharp income drops result in substantially higher mortality risk, even when such financial setbacks are only temporary.

We know that stress can affect our mental and physical health. It is no surprise that financial problems cause people to neglect their health, and that the stress of financial problems may harm your health.

Here are a few examples:

- A study by the State University of New York at Buffalo, published in the Journal of Periodontology, documented the association between financial stress and gum disease. About 30 million Americans suffer from gum disease, a bacterial infection, which has been associated with an increased risk of heart attack and stroke.

- Dr. Fred Waddel is a nationally recognized expert who helps people to eliminate compulsive spending and to monitor attitudes and habits that may result in financial problems. He states that clients with financial problems often had lower back problems and eating disorders.

- In her best-selling book, *Heal Your Body*, Louise Hay identified the following physical maladies that accompany money problems: lower back problems, slipped discs, sciatica, and obesity. A recent study confirmed that individuals who live in psychosocially stressful environments were more susceptible to lower back disorders.

- Caroline Myss, a medical intuitive, is the author of *Anatomy of the Spirit: The Seven Stages of Power and Healing*. In the section titled, "The Energy of Money," she wrote: "A scarcity of money translates into a scarcity of energy in the body itself – again unconsciously. The misperception of money as the life force, coupled with a sudden loss of money, can activate any of several health crises: prostate cancer, impotence, endometriosis, ovarian problems, lower back and sciatic pain..."

Cases histories illustrating the health impact of financial problems:

Case #1: Veronica, a 54-year-old menopausal patient on hormone replacement therapy, complained that she was having difficulty sleeping. She has been my patient for many years. Veronica was hesitant to discuss this, as she knew that it would be difficult to convince me to prescribe sleeping pills. It took some probing before I learned that she recently received a letter from the IRS; she and her husband owed more than $70,000 in back taxes and penalties. A week later, I read an article about bargaining with the IRS. I sent it to her and she and the IRS finally arrived at an agreeable compromise. Her usual sleeping pattern resumed soon afterward.

Case #2: Barbara is a 48-year old teacher, good friend and patient. She and I usually celebrate our birthdays together in March, during Women Make History week, when I would also speak to her class. This has been a ritual for us for more than 13 years. One year we celebrated her birthday in April, and I realized that I had not spoken to her class. Through her tears, Barbara told me that she did not want to be a teacher any longer. I was shocked. Barbara confessed that she was tired of the politics at the school; politics that made teachers not want to teach. To make matters worse, her financial adviser told her she could not retire until she was 55. Barbara felt trapped. She had been feeling depressed and could not shake a lingering cold. This situation did not improve until Barbara found a way to earn additional income. The extra income gave her the freedom to retire when she wanted, and she regained her love of teaching.

Case #3. Regina, a 37-year-old supervisor at a small company, reported irregular bleeding over the course of three months. About six months before, she overheard rumors that her company was on the verge of closing its doors. Regina was a single parent with two small children who earned a good income, but the country was in a recession. She feared becoming unemployed, being unable to pay her bills, and losing her house. One woman in five will experience irregular or heavy bleeding due to under-active thyroid. If the TSH (thyroid-stimulating hormone) level is low, thyroid supplements may resolve the problem. Regina's TSH level was within normal limits. Another reason for irregular bleeding, in the absence of a pathological reason, is stress. Regina did lose her job but was able to find another one right away. Her periods became regular again.

Case #4. Ingrid, a 26-year-old woman, came to my office complaining about loss of sexual desire. A year before she had given birth to a healthy son. She said that she and her husband rarely had sex any more. Both Ingrid and her husband had problems with spending. In fewer than four years, they had accumulated credit card debt of $26,000, at 19.9% interest. Her husband had a good job, but they were having difficulty making ends meet and were sinking deeper in debt. They each blamed the other. Ingrid's exam and blood work were within normal limits. In her case, she and her husband needed the help of a debt counselor to resolve their problems.

Case #5. Debra, a 52-year-old woman, was having difficulty sleeping and was experiencing hot flashes. She had been taking hormone replacement therapy since she started menopause. Debra wanted me to increase her medication dosage. It has been my experience that when a medication stops working after it has been working well for a while, something big is happening in the woman's life. I cannot quote scientific studies to prove this, but this has been true for many of my patients. My theory is that stress may cause some drugs to be more readily metabolized by the body, and the usual dose may not be as effective as before. It may be logical to increase the dose, but this is not done without increasing risk. In Debra's case, she lived with an abusive husband. She knew that she had to leave; the children were grown. Debra's problem was that she had allowed her husband to make all financial decisions. She had no skills, and felt she would be unable to survive on her own if she left her husband.

Case #6. May is a 56-year-old woman who was experiencing unusual heart palpitations. Otherwise, she was healthy. For several months she served as her 88 year-old mother's sole caregiver. Her mother was having problems with senility and did not want to live in a retirement home or with May. The mother owned a small home and was on Medicare; she did not have long-term care insurance. Since one out of every two women dies of heart disease each year, I referred her to a cardiologist to rule out heart disease. Her cardiac evaluation was normal. May's symptoms subsided after she found help for her mother's care.

Some financial problems that can affect physical and mental health are poverty, unstable income, excessive debt, and lack of health insurance.

Studies have demonstrated that poverty, disparity of income, and unemployment, are some of the most damaging portions of the health equation. If you are barely able to make ends meet, preventive health care becomes a luxury – especially when paying for a doctor's visit uses money allotted for food.

In my home country of Haiti, where the per capita yearly income is only $340, life expectancy is only 45 years. In areas of the US where there are large numbers of poor, statistics reveal that mortality is similar to many third-world countries. Less than half of Americans get the most beneficial disease preventing services in medicine, says a study funded by the Centers for Disease Control. Clearly, poverty has a significant impact on health and longevity.

People who live outside of the US may not understand that people struggle in America, the land of opportunity. *What causes many Americans to end up in dire financial situations?* I do not pretend to know the answer, but, in my humble opinion, it has to do with our relationship with money, as well as the ability of each of us to grab opportunities to receive an education, get a job, and save money.

🌿

RETIREMENT INEQUITIES

The likelihood that a woman's quality of life will be downgraded as the result of inadequate retirement income or long-term chronic illness is highly probable. Either women are not taking heed or they are not learning how to prepare for their later years. Women have come a long way and account for 49.4% of first-year law students in 2000 compared to 10% in 1970, 46% of medical students in 2000, and received 38% of MBA degrees awarded in 1998. In spite of increasing numbers of female law graduates, the proportion of female judges and law firm partners has not kept pace.

Beginning in the late 1960s, women advanced in the work force in earnest. According to the 2000 Census Bureau figures, while nearly as many women as men have college degrees, men far outnumber women in high-paying jobs. Thirteen percent of men aged 15 and older earn more than $75,000 annually, and 19% earn $50,000 to $74,000 annually. Only 4% of women of the same ages earned more than $75,000 and 9% earned $50,000 to $74,000 annually.

Women often outlive their male counterparts and experience poverty during their later years. The average age of widowhood is 56. Approximately 80% of retired women lack pension benefits because they are typically employed in settings that do not offer retirement benefits. A full-time working woman over the age of 45 has two-thirds the median earning capacity of men the same age.

According to the US Census Bureau, women are continuing to move to the forefront of US business, especially in California. However, women-owned businesses tend to be smaller than those owned by men, and many small business owners have no health insurance or have high deductibles and co-pays, no disability insurance, and no retirement plan.

ΨΨΡ̂ρ̂

THE CHANGING FACE OF HOMELESSNESS

The fastest growing subgroup of the American homeless is women. Almost 5% (5.7 million) of Americans are homeless. Homelessness has been defined as lacking "fixed, regular, and adequate night-time residence," and occurs when income falls short of expenses for shelter. The cause of homelessness is different for men and women, but insufficient affordable housing is the single largest contributor. Poverty and physical and sexual trauma typically propel women into homelessness. If a woman loses her home due to sudden calamity, she may receive emergency assistance and emotional support, but if a woman loses her home gradually due to poverty, or by fleeing an abusive relationship, far less assistance is available.

There is a tendency for us to believe that the homeless suffer from mental illness, especially following the de-institutionalization of the mentally ill in the 1950s and 1960s. In fact, reports indicate that only about 30% of the homeless suffer from mental illness, and 50% to 60% of these are women. Mental disorders are a normal response to chronic trauma, and not evidence of primary mental illness. Studies have estimated that approximately 16% to 26% of homeless women abuse drugs or alcohol.

I have attended to patients at the Rachel Women's Center, a homeless shelter in San Diego operated by the Catholic Charities, since 1985. In 1997, I began attending patients at St. Vincent de Paul Village, another homeless shelter in San Diego. I have never forgotten my first encounter with Betty, a homeless woman.

Betty was about my age, had a home, a husband, and a job. First, her husband died of a severe illness, then she began to have health problems, she lost her job, and finally she lost her home. There were some night shelters in the city, but often, there were not enough beds. Betty had been homeless for six months, occasionally slept in Balboa Park, and had been raped.

I was shocked to discover that many homeless women are women just like you and me. I have since met many women and men just like Betty and they all have one thing in common: *financial difficulties.*

The "traditional" homeless person is a young to middle-aged individual, who has difficulties due to unemployment, mental health, or alcohol or drug addiction. *Senior citizens represent the newest subgroup of homeless.* Once they retire, many members of the middle class find themselves reduced to poverty and live in decrepit hotels or become homeless.

To illustrate: According to the San Diego County Apartment Association, the average rent for a one-bedroom apartment in San Diego County is $640. For many seniors social security provides them income of $700 per month. Subsidized housing for the poor is lacking in San Diego. The newly homeless individual typically has no savings, has lost a job, has outlived their resources due to increased cost of living, has no relatives to turn to, and ends up living on the street or in homeless shelters.

Do you wonder how long you'll live in retirement? In 2002 there are approximately 72,000 centenarians in the US. *According to the US Census, there could be anywhere from 265,000 to more than 4 million people who are 100 years old by the year 2050!* Currently the averages are: a healthy 65-year-old woman has a 44% chance of living to age 90, and the chances that one member of a healthy couple, both 65 years old will live to age 84, are 87%. What will your quality of life be in advanced age? Longer lifespans mean you may outlive your savings *unless you plan ahead.* Plan as if you will live in retirement for at least two decades.

🌱🌱🌱

EFFECTIVE PLANNING

Everyone knows planning for the future is important. We plan what we will study in college. We plan appropriate exercise in order to achieve physical strength and endurance. We even plan in order to take that family vacation. *Yet, many of us do not plan for our financial future.* Would you believe people spend more time planning their annual vacation than they spend planning their financial future? And, when something does go wrong, even if it is a minor problem, we are caught unprepared and emotionally unable to handle the impact. We worry and our health suffers as a result of the additional stress. Deep down, we understand that we need to eat balanced meals and exercise regularly in order to maintain our health. Excellent health is the result of careful, day-to-day attention to nutrition and exercise. The same principle holds true for our financial health.

You owe it to yourself to talk to a financial expert. I do have some tips to get you started. And, remember what I said, your *financial health is related to your overall health*. So make the decision today to become proactive about your financial health!

Here are some steps that have worked for me, and this "prescription" may work well for you, too. Each step is important, and all must be coordinated for you to succeed.

Step I: Assess Your Current Financial Health

What is personal financial planning? *It is a process, not a product*. It is an organized system of developing strategies for using your financial resources to achieve both short – and long-term goals. Evaluating your current financial situation is the first step in developing any financial plan.

The following worksheet is designed to help you by clearly outlining your assets and liabilities. Your net worth is the major measurement of your wealth, and is calculated by subtracting your liabilities from your assets. By increasing your assets or reducing your debt you increase your net worth. *Do you know what you're worth?*

Calculate Your Net Worth

Assets

Savings and Investments

Cash (money in the bank, checking, savings, money market deposit accounts) .... $_____

CDs (Certificates of Deposit) .... $_____

Income Investments (stocks, bonds, mutual funds) .... $_____

Real Estate Investment .... $_____

Ownership Interest in a Business,
Partnership or Other Investments .... $_____

Other .... $_____

Retirement Plan Investments

Individual Retirement Accounts (IRAs) .... $_____

SEP .... $_____

Keogh Plan .... $_____

401(k) or 403(b) Plans .... $_____

Pension Plan .... $_____

Profit Sharing Plan .... $_____

Cash Value of Life Insurance .... $_____

Market Value of Home(s) .... $_____

Personal Property .... $_____
(cars, collectibles, furniture, jewelry)

Other .... $_____

Total Assets .... *$*_____

Liabilities

Mortgage Payment ....$_____

Car Loans ....$_____

Credit Cards ....$_____

Student Loans ....$_____

Other Loans ....$_____

Unpaid Taxes ....$_____

Outstanding Bills and Obligations ....$_____

Total Liabilities ....$_____

Your Net Worth (Assets minus Liabilities)

Total Assets $_____

Total Liabilities $_____

Total Net Worth $_____

If you recently graduated from college and have student loans, your liabilities may exceed your assets. Whatever your net worth is – positive or negative – the most important fact is that you are now *aware* of your financial picture and are willing to work on it. Remember, it is never too late to start and no amount is too little to save!

Often, people count on income tax refunds to pay for a vacation or a down payment on a car. If you receive a fairly large income tax refund each year, your employer is withholding too much from your paycheck. That tax refund may seem like a windfall, but you are not looking at the situation correctly. Overpaying taxes is like giving the IRS an interest-free loan. If this money was not withheld from your paycheck, you could save it or use it to pay off debts. Ask your tax preparer or someone in your accounting or benefits department to help you calculate your withholdings.

Step II: Know How Much You Spend

Sometimes we are unable to save because we are unaware of how much we spend. When I started working with a financial advisor, I filled out a Monthly Family Expense Budget. I was surprised to realize that my weekly tennis lessons were costing me $2,600 per year. I took the time to find a tennis partner, reduced my lessons to one per week, and saved $1,300.

I know a woman who loved café latte and bought one every workday at lunchtime. She did not realize that the $4.25 she spent each day added up to $1,100 a year. Had she invested this money, earning an average of 7% per year, she would have had about $80,000, enough to buy her own coffee franchise. Makes you think, doesn't it!

I've included a *Monthly Family Expense Budget* worksheet, located at the back of the book, to help you determine your monthly family expense budget. It will help you to budget your spending and saving. *Please use it!*

Step III: Establish Your Financial Goals

I advise you to establish financial goals for yourself, and if applicable, your family. A financial goal is how you want to your finances to look. Where do you want to be in 5 years? How about 10 years? Or 20? Having a clear goal and the willingness to work hard can make it happen. If you can imagine and plan it, you can achieve it. Setting specific goals also helps you to determine the amount of money you need to meet each goal. With specific goals in mind, you can estimate a time frame within which each goal will be realized.

Examples of specific goals:

- I want to have enough money to retire when I am 55.
- I want to save money for my children to go to college.
- I want to pay off my credit card debts.
- I want to save money so I can enjoy a comfortable retirement.
- I want to leave a financial legacy for my heirs.
- I want to save money for a new car.
- I want to pay off my college loans.
- I want to save money to make a down-payment on a house.

Step IV: List Your Financial Goals

Goal	Amt. Needed	Time Frame
1._____	$_____	_____
2._____	$_____	_____
3._____	$_____	_____
4._____	$_____	_____

Step V: Learn "Saving Skills"

There are three types of obligations. *Discretionary obligations* include entertainment, vacations, and hobbies. *Variable obligations* consist of insurance, food, clothing, telephone service, electricity, water, and other household necessities. *Fixed obligations* include mortgage payments or rent and other loans and obligations. Although it may not be easy, we can reduce our discretionary expenditures. They may be absorbing a large chunk of our income.

I often hear women say, "there is no extra money," or "we don't have enough money." These same people spend $50 or more a week on their families at the movie theatre. Yes, we are entitled to a night of enjoyment now and then. If this family went to the movies every other week, they could save $100 a month. Or, they could go to a drive-in theatre, take their own snacks, and save a bundle! You can set a good example for the children by proving that family outings do not have to cost an arm and a leg. Further, if you deposited a portion of this saving into college funds for your children, you just might teach them a few lessons in frugality. Resourceful family planning can yield savings that ensure a more comfortable future, and a healthier lifestyle with less worry and stress.

Step VI: Create a Comprehensive Savings Plan.

Once you create a financial plan, you will know what you need to do and when you need to do it. You will better understand the financial decisions you need to make and the impact of these decisions on your future financial freedom. Having a financial plan in place helps to eliminate excess stress and worry. There is no better time than right now to work on financial balance in your life.

Creating a financial plan may sound difficult, but with clear goals, you will be well on your way.

Your savings plan should include three components:

- A savings account balance 3 to 6 times your monthly family expense budget.

- Personal savings and investments through IRA, Roth IRA and others.

- Saving and investments through a retirement plan at work – 401(k) or 403(b) plan if you are an employee, a defined-benefit plan, or SET if you are self-employed.

Personal Savings

Saving money has little to do with how much you earn.

How much you save is largely dependent upon your ability to save. Even though financial freedom is at stake, few of us have been *taught* to save. Many of us want instant gratification and have yet to acquire the discipline to save as we struggle each day to make ends meet. We also have bad habits. When we get a raise, we buy a bigger home, a nicer car, take nicer vacations, or buy a second home, instead of saving some of it. It's costly to keep up with the Joneses.

One is never too old to start saving. And, even the smallest amount of money saved will grow over a long period of time. Having your own personal nest egg can make a big difference in how you handle minor or major lifestyle crises, and will determine how well you will live after you retire. It is also important to understand that because we are living longer, your retirement savings may have to provide for your needs for some 20-30 years beyond retirement. Social Security is not a complete retirement plan and benefits are not intended as your sole source of income. And, as you may have heard, Social Security may not be there when you need it. So, let's go over some ideas to pad your savings.

Pay Yourself First

You owe it to yourself to make regular savings a priority. Just like you pay your rent, mortgage, and taxes, you should *pay yourself by saving*. According to Derek Dingle of Black Enterprise Magazine, "paying oneself first should become everyone's loud-and-clear mantra, and the earlier, the better." The first principle of Black Enterprise's Declaration of Financial Empowerment suggests that we save and invest 10% to 15% of our after-tax income. By letting the magic of compounding work for you, you lay the foundation for serious wealth down the road.

Saving 10% to 15% of your income may be impossible for some people. Maybe you are able to save only $25 a month. The important thing is to save regularly, regardless of how much or how little it is. The sooner you start, the easier it will be for you to achieve your financial goals. If you find that you are having difficulty disciplining yourself to save each month, then you might want to ask your bank or credit union about setting up an automatic withdrawal from checking to your savings account.

You need to save enough money to cover 3 to 6 months of living expenses. This money should be kept in a liquid emergency fund, one that may be converted to cash quickly and easily, and without significant penalties.

Saving on Your Home

The rule of thumb is that the price of a new home should not exceed two times your annual income. Monthly expenses associated with the home, such as the mortgage payment, any maintenance costs, utility bills, and repairs, should not exceed 38% of your after-tax income. Many first-time buyers fail to realize that after coming up with the down-payment, they also need to pay closing costs. Ask your lender to estimate closing costs before making any final decisions.

- If you are lucky enough to realize the American dream of owning your own home, you may be able to save money in the following ways: Consider refinancing your mortgage. You should do this when mortgage rates drop 2 or more percentage points below what you are currently paying. If you plan to stay in your home long-term, you may wish to refinance if mortgage rates drop one percentage point below your interest rate.
- A home equity loan may be used to pay off high interest credit card debt, thereby reducing your monthly payments. Equity loan interest rates are usually much lower than credit card rates, and interest paid on an equity loan may be tax-deductible for federal income-tax purposes. Interest payments on credit card debts are not tax-deductible

Saving on Your Car

The purchase of a new car is the second largest financial decision you may have to make in your life. Unless you finance the car at a very low rate, you may opt to pay for your car through a home equity loan if you are a homeowner. Shop around and consider purchasing a used car. Some car models may have secret factory warranties that cover problems or repairs common to particular car models. To find out if your car has such warranty, send a self-address stamped business-sized envelope to The Center for Auto Safety, 2001 S St. NW, Washington DC 20009. Be sure to provide the year, make and model of your car. Following are some strategies involving insurance that reduce the costs of owning a car:

- You may qualify for a discount of up to 20% of the cost of insurance covering two or more cars.

- You may qualify for a "good driver" discount if you have not had an accident or moving violation in the last three to five years.

- Your teenage driver may qualify for a 20% discount if they take who driving education classes.

- Having a car alarm can save you as much as 20%.

- If your car is 7 or more years old, you may not need collision or comprehensive coverage. Collision insurance pays the cost of replacing or repairing your car in the event of an accident, whether you are at fault or not. Comprehensive insurance covers the cost of fixing your car if it is damaged by flood, wind, fire, or if it is stolen.

- Select high deductibles. You can shave approximately 15% off the premium by increasing your deductible from $100 to $200. You save 25% by raising your deductible to $500 and 33% by raising it further to $1000. This only makes sense if you can afford to pay the deductible.

Saving on your Taxes

Keep copies of this year's tax documents to refresh your memory about deductions and any carry-forwards and losses. Expand your list of itemized deductions. The tax code is full of deductions you may not know about, and they change periodically. If you own your home, make your January house payment the December before, to have an additional month of mortgage interest to deduct. Avoid investment funds that have a history of distributing capital gains and dividends to reduce taxable income.

Buying Smart

Many times we purchase things on sale just because it is a great deal. I was shopping with a friend who saw a beautiful sweater selling at 50% off. She liked the idea so much that she purchased two in her favorite colors. Where were her savings?

- Just because something is on sale does not mean that you have to buy it.
- By setting aside a *spending allowance* that you can afford, you may be able to give yourself small rewards for not exceeding your budget.
- Keep your eye out for items that you need far in advance. Watch for sales held at different times during the year.
- Above all, make it a habit to save for something, rather than purchasing it with high-interest credit cards.

Saving for College

The Economic Growth and Tax Relief Reconciliation Act, passed by Congress in 2001, boosted education savings accounts (formerly Education IRAs) from $500 to $2,000. Prepaying your mortgage may not be a good idea if your child is applying to colleges because home equity is considered an asset by college financial aid administrators. Invest the extra money in retirement plans, which will not affect your child's financial aid prospects.

Learn more about saving for college in *New Strategies for College Funding,* written by Raymond D. Loewe, CLU, DhFC, and K. C. Dempster.

Personal Investments Savings

Whether you are an employee or are self-employed you can take advantage of a variety of saving options. As of this writing, you may contribute up to $3,000 per person to a tax-deductible IRA if you earn less than $100,000 annually. Or you may wish to invest in stocks, bonds, mutual funds, or certificates of deposit.

Saving Through Employment

Most people need to save at least 10% of their annual income in order to retire with their current inflation-adjusted income. *Few people save enough.* It used to be that employers paid into traditional retirement plans that guaranteed retirement income for their employees. Now, we have 401(k) and 403(b) plans that require employee contributions, although employees also get to choose how their money is invested. Employees must have sufficient knowledge to make these decisions.

Employees now must face the fact that retirement may come much later in life due to dwindling returns in retirement funds and insufficient savings. The age for retirement has been pushed back to the late 60's or early 70's. The life expectancy for 65-year-old Americans is 84 years. In order to receive 60%

of pre-retirement income through age 84, an employee needs to work and save until age 69.5, assuming that Social Security covers the other 40%.

One way to save for your future is to take advantage of employer contributions. Many companies allow an employee to defer 10% to 15% of their gross pay to a 401(k) plan. Let us assume that an employer matches the first 6% of employee contributions, chipping in 50 cents for each dollar an employee contributes. If an employee earns $40,000 a year, her employer would contribute $1,200 (6 % of $40,000 x 50 cents). When your employer matches your contribution with 50 cents for each dollar you invest in your 401(k), you realize an immediate 50% return on your money.

The Economic Growth and Tax Relief Reconciliation Act, passed by Congress in 2001, allows Americans aged 50 and older to save even more in the form of "catch-up" contributions to IRAs and 401(k) plans. (At the time of this writing, California has not passed a bill supporting this increase.)

Your employer may offer company stock as part of your 401(k). If the company performs well financially, your investment should perform well. But, if the company does not perform well, such as Enron, you could lose some or all of your money. It is highly recommended that you not invest more than 20% of your portfolio with your employer. You also need to be aware that management fees for 401(k) plans can be as high as 3%.

- Increase your retirement plan contribution each time you receive a pay raise.
- If you have to leave your job, do not cash in your retirement plan. It is intended for use after you retire. You will pay substantial penalties if you cash it in, so consider leaving the money where it is, moving it to your new employer's plan, or rolling it over into an IRA.

Saving Through Personal Business

If you are self-employed, take advantage of deductible IRA contributions of up to 2,000 per person, or $4,000 per couple, if your income is less than $100,000 annually. Annual allowable contributions are supposed to increase within the next 5 years. The self-employed person has a variety of retirement plan options to choose from. Your financial advisor can help you choose the best one for your situation.

Buyer Beware

Whether you are an employee or are self-employed, you need to take charge of your retirement account. Many companies invest the majority of retirement plan assets in company stock. When Enron's stock dropped from $80 a share to less than $1 a share within a year, thousands of employees lost the majority of their 401(k) retirement plan.

Here are some recommendations:

- Diversify your portfolio with a mixture of bonds, mutual funds and diversified stocks.
- Invest no more than 20% of your retirement plan in your employer's stocks.
- Consult independent analyses from agencies like Value Line, Standard & Poor, and Moody.
- Avoid stocks for which accounting issues have been raised.
- Consider listening to public-access analyst conference calls, available on the Internet.
- Consider hiring a fee-only financial planner.
- Save first and spend the balance. Do not spend first and save what is left over, because there is never anything left over!

If you are eligible for Social Security retirement income, each year, three months prior to your birthday, you will receive a statement of your future benefits. You can obtain this information any time at www.ssa.gov/mystatement/index.htm.

Asset Allocation

We have all heard the saying "Don't put all your eggs into one basket." Diversifying your portfolio reduces your risk of losing the full value of your investments. The process of deciding what percentage of your money to put in each type of investment is called asset allocation. Your age, savings goal, investment time-frame, and amount of risk you are willing to take, will determine your asset allocation. The purpose of this book is not to teach you how to invest, but to encourage you to learn. Your financial advisor will be your best guide and teacher.

Educate Yourself about Investment Options

There is an array of retirement-savings vehicles, but they can be confusing. Learn about the various types of investments in order to make the wisest financial decisions.

Here are some investment options.

Bonds

A bond is a debt instrument, like an IOU, that is issued by a party who promises to pay a specific rate of interest for a specified time period, and repay the principal on a specified date (also called the maturity date). Bonds are used to raise capital by entities such as individual cities and states, corporations, and the Federal government. *Municipal bonds* are bonds issued by states, municipalities, or state agencies or authorities for the sole purpose of funding governmental functions. Any interest paid on municipal bonds is exempt from federal income tax.

Individual Retirement Account (IRA)

An IRA is a tax-favored retirement account that allows an individual to contribute up to a certain amount each year of annual earnings (up to $3,000 in 2002). Contributions may be tax deductible, subject to Modified Adjust Gross Income limits. Money invested in IRAs is tax-deferred until withdrawn, usually starting at age 59.5 or older.

Roth IRA

Established in the Taxpayer Relief Act of 1997, the Roth IRA allows an individual to save for retirement while allowing the savings to grow tax-free, subject to certain income limits. Taxes are paid on contributions, but withdrawals are tax-free, if certain rules are met. IRA contributions may be made up to April 15 of the following calendar year. There is a 10% penalty if the funds are withdrawn before age 59.5.

Keogh Plan

A Keogh Plan, or self-employed pension plan (SEP), is a tax-deferred qualified retirement plan for self-employed individuals and unincorporated businesses.

Money Market

The money market is the market for borrowing and lending large amounts of short-term funds. Money market instruments include negotiable certificates of deposit, notes,

Treasury bills, and the like.

Money Market Accounts

These are federally-insured accounts at banks or other financial institutions that pay rates established by the institution based upon money market yields.

Money Market Mutual Funds

Money market mutual funds are similar to money market accounts but are not federally insured.

Money Market Deposit Accounts

This is a liquid account offered by banks or credit unions that typically provides a higher interest rate than that of a savings account. The account is FDIC insured and its rate of interest is usually sensitive to changes in market rates. The FDIC is a federal agency that insures deposit member banks and other financial institutions up to $100,000.

Mutual Funds

A mutual fund is administered by an investment company and enables shareholders to pool funds for professional management as a single investment account.

Stock

Ownership of a stock represents ownership in a company. The value of stocks fluctuates with a company's performance and the stock market in general. Occasional stock

scandals can make stocks look dangerous and scare investors. Indeed, some individual stocks are higher risk investments and should be carefully considered. Even leading
market experts can't always predict when to buy and when
to sell. Choose your strategy with the advice of trained professionals, then stick to it. By the way, it is an "urban myth"
that the stock market goes up when skirt lengths rise, and
down when hemlines lengthen!

Stock Funds

A stock fund is a mutual fund invested in many stocks. It
offers investors diversification and professional management.

Finances and Your Mate

Marriage is an economic relationship, a personal business
partnership, regardless of whether it's a one- or two-income household. According to Ginita Wall, CPA, CFP, 550 divorces take place
for every 1,000 marriages. *Financial differences or difficulties
are the most common causes of divorce.* Many educated women
leave financial decisions to their spouse. I know many women who
found themselves in the poorhouse because their spouse squandered money that could have been saved.

Money problems are often at the root of marital
troubles. In fact, financial stress – caused by lack of money or
disagreement over how to manage it is not only the number
one cause of domestic discord, the reverse is also true – unhappy marriages tend to become financially unstable. Money
is sometimes used as a weapon, and some games played are
"yours" and "mine" view of funds, spite spending, secret
hoarding, and secret spending. In the end, no one wins.

Women should be aware of all financial transactions
made by the couple or family. Whether money is squandered

or badly invested, ignorance of family finances can be very costly. *Even with Social Security, older women are two times as likely as older men to be poor.*

You may have good intentions but have a partner with dreadful money management habits. Women should know the laws concerning marriage in the state in which they live. California and Florida are community property states, meaning that each spouse owns half of all property amassed during the marriage, regardless of who earned it. Debts are also community property. According Betty Crowther, a real estate broker, "many women with good credit are unable to purchase a house because of their partner's lifestyle and bad credit history." Betty suggests that a woman considering marriage needs more than proof of her partner's negative HIV status – she also needs to see her partner's credit history.

Every woman should be able to discuss the family finances with her mate without the subject ending in an argument. Many women are unaware of their husband's business, loans, debts, or assets. Part of a woman's financial education is to learn all of the above and to participate in financial decision-making. Strengthen the financial partnership with your mate by analyzing your own and each other's attitudes toward money, and *write down mutual goals*. Spend a few minutes each week to pay bills together and to discuss how *each member* of your family is spending money.

If you are getting married and you have assets of children, you should consider consulting with a lawyer concerning a prenuptial agreement.

Educate Your Children

I believe it is of paramount importance to teach your children about money and credit. According to Kathleen Gurney, Ph.D., an internationally-known researcher, author, and pioneer in the study of the psychology of money and investing, "financial education is just as important as teaching someone to read and write." Financial education early in life can help prevent financial problems.

Young children do not intuitively understand what you mean when you say you cannot afford to buy them something they want. Less than one-quarter of high school students are taking courses in personal finance. *You* have to teach them.

One day, my 5-year-old nephew told my sister Elsie that it was easy to get money. "You just have to stick a card in the wall and money comes out." Shawn had seen his mother getting money this way at an ATM. It took some explaining, but he finally understood that in order to get the money out of the wall, Elsie had to put money in the bank. Another misunderstanding involved my sister Marise, a single parent, and her children. Kisha and Sammy were teenagers and always seemed to want something Marise could not afford. One day, she showed her children her pay stubs, her child-support checks, and her monthly budget. There were no more demands.

Teens in the US are wealthy. They spend $89 billion a year on such goodies as entertainment, clothes and food. But that total also includes big-ticket items, according to surveys conducted by Teenage Research Unlimited. Over half own televisions and 35% have their own VCRs. Fully 30% have bought their own car or truck. But, the scary fact is that the majority of teens don't know the first thing about money – how to manage, save or spend it wisely. They'll be on their own in a few years. They need to know some valuable real-world lessons about money, before they're teens..

According to a survey of 2001 college graduates, 90% feel strongly that they are likely to get what they want in life. Money tops the list of things they hope to not have problems with, but only 8% reported to have any knowledge about financial or retirement planning. In order to change this pattern, financial education needs to begin early in life in order to prevent serious future financial problems.

Have a credit card talk with your children before they reach 18. Explain to them how easy it is to get into debt and how difficult it is to pay it off. Consider getting a "secured" credit card (credit is limited to the amount of money you put up to open the account) to start your teens personal credit history and to give them supervised experience with credit decisions.

According to Valerie Jacobs, a San Diego psychologist and wealth counselor, "It is not the money, it's how you raise your children." Children need to learn how money is earned. They should understand the concept of relative value, or the cost of an item relative to what it takes to pay for it. Help your child to understand that they would have to wash dishes every day for the next six months in order to earn the money to buy a desired toy.

Children should not be afraid to talk about good and bad practices concerning money. Teach children about wants and needs and teach them money management skills. Decide which chores you feel comfortable paying your children to do for you and pay them an allowance based on what they accomplish. Specific chores may include taking out the garbage, weeding the garden, or washing dishes. Have your children set aside 10% to 15% of their allowance for savings and investments. Teach your teens budgeting basics and help them create a personal budget.

Help them set up a savings account when they are young and insist that they save a portion – even if it's small – of all money gifts, allowances, baby-sitting and any other income. At least until they're 18, insist on accountability of how money is spent. High schoolers should have checkbooks and be shown how to use and balance them. *Discuss money matters with your children.* Help them understand that successful money management takes self-discipline and planning.

For young people, the key to accumulating wealth is to use *time* to their advantage. Cheryl D. Broussard, financial advisor and author of the *Black Woman's Guide to Financial Independence*, says, "If you have only a small amount of money to invest and you are young, you have the ingredients essential to becoming financially independent."

Financial programs for young people include:

- Kidpreneurs Conference by *Black Enterprise* teaches children financial principles. Their advice includes: teaching children to invest early through mutual funds and investment clubs; parents sharing with their children to allocate dollars to meet fixed and variable expenses in a budget; giving stock and mutual funds as gifts; and making money management fun. www.blackenterprise.com

- *Money Mentors* provides practical information for parents of children of all ages who are interested in teaching their children good money management skills. www.moneymentors.net

- *Springboard* offers education on the wise use of credit and offers assistance as an alternative to bankruptcy. www.credit.org

- *GE Center for Financial Learning* can be found at www.financiallearning.com.

- *Dollar Digest* is a publication that features comprehensive interviews with company CEOs and profiles on the financial performance of companies in kid-friendly terms.

Also please consider:

- Giving gifts of shares of stock to your children and grandchildren instead of traditional gifts for birthdays and holidays.
- Helping your children learn about their investments by teaching them how to keep track of the value of their stocks and mutual funds.
- Involve your children in an investment club. The National Association of Investors Corporation (NAIC) provides a kit to help children to be organized.
- Play games such as Monopoly, or Cash Flow from Robert T. Kiyosaki.
- Subscribe to KidpreneursNewsäor Black Enterprise for Teensä newsletter. These entities are dedicated to teaching your children business essentials. Call 1-877-543-7736.

Step VII: Get Rid of Your Debts

According to a student loan agency, 78% of college students have credit cards with an average debt of $2,750. *One in five college students were forced to move in with their parents or friends because of debt and other financial issues.*

According to a survey undertaken by the GE Center for Financial Learning, one in three young adults, age 18 to 29, owes an average of $5,000 to $50,000, and almost 60% of them reported to have carried up to $25,000 in consumer debt. Forty percent of teenagers forgo college and face adult financial decisions without any financial knowledge.

Adults do not fare any better. According to the experts, 70% of working Americans have no money left after paying basic expenses and bills each month. According to the Federal Reserve Board, adults save too little and spend too much, amassing about $9,000 in consumer debt per household. In addition to owning a home, they want the works – clothing, cars, the latest gadgets, and luxury vacations, even though they cannot afford them.

It is not difficult to find news stories about rising debt and de-creased savings rates. In the year 2001, Americans depleted their savings at record levels. Personal savings, or your disposable personal income less personal spending, fell to the lowest level since economists began calculating the figure in 1959. The days are gone when borrowing money was difficult and something to be avoided! Today, getting into debt is simple, but getting out of it is another story altogether. Even young adults just entering the work force find plenty of credit available to them. When debt is taken on early in life, it is even more difficult to eliminate, and the impact and stress may last for years.

As debt increases, so does your stress level. Under stress, your ability to handle a financial crisis is impacted and health problems can occur. These health problems can result in days lost from work, and affect job and income stability.

Your first priority should be to pay off your credit card and student loan debt. Pay off your credit card accounts with the highest interest rates first. Not having to shell out 20% to 30% interest on credit card debt is as good as a savings return of 20% to 30% tax-free. Pay more than the minimum amount due toward your credit card balance monthly. Pay on time to avoid late fees, which can run as high as $30.

In a study released in March 2002, the New York's Cambridge Consumer Credit Corporation revealed that consumers are not only going deeply into debt, they are not paying off that debt at an acceptable rate. Cambridge supervises a poll of 1,000 Americans each and then compiles its consumer index credit report. According to the study, 47% of those who did not pay their balance in full only paid the minimum amount.

Do not carry more than two credit cards. Transfer high balances to a lower rate card – and when you switch cards, close out the old one and request they report to major credit bureaus that the account has been closed. Too many open credit card accounts may make it difficult to get a new card.

Have a credit card talk with your children before they reach

18. Explain to them how easy it is to get into debt and how difficult it is to pay it off. Consider getting a "secured" credit card (credit is limited to the amount of money you put up to open the account) to start your teens personal credit history and to give them supervised experience with credit decisions.

If possible, consolidate your debts into one account with a lower interest rate. If you own a home, consider paying off your credit card debt with a lower-interest home equity loan. *Interest paid on a home-equity loan may be tax-deductible while interest paid toward credit cards is not.* If you do not own a home, consider applying for a low interest credit card with a higher credit limit. Whatever you do, do not borrow from your retirement fund to pay off debt.

It is recommended that you check your credit report and your medical report every 12 to 18 months, since the information contained in these reports may be incorrect. You can order a copy of your credit report from:

1. *Experian (formerly TRW),* POB 8030, Layton, UT 84041-8030 1-800-392-1122
2. *Equifax,* POB 105873, Atlanta, GA 30348 1-800-685-1111 Purchase a credit profile online for $9 at www.equifax.org
3. *TransUnion* Consumer Disclosure Center , POB 1000, Chester, PA 19022 1-316-636-6100

Request a copy of your medical file from *The Medical Information Bureau* POB 105, Essex Station, Boston, MA 02112. Telephone 1-617-426-3660

Credit Card Crunch

Late payments affect more than your credit rating, they affect your pocketbook. Due to rising interest rates, an increasing number of people are sinking deeper into debt, which can take decades to pay off. The average American household carries about $7,500 in credit-card debit, enough to cripple the ability to save.

Most credit card contracts warn customers that their interest rates will increase if they fall behind on their payments. A growing number of credit card holders are paying interest rates as high as 30% after missing a single payment deadline. Late fees can be as high as $30, so develop the habit of paying your bills at least a week before they are due.

Here is an example of what you might experience if you were to miss one credit card payment deadline. If you owed $3,000 at an interest rate of *7.9%,* it would take you 10 years and 11 months to pay the account off, if you made the minimum monthly payment. You would have paid $793.94 in interest.

At *18.9%* – the average credit card interest rate – it would take you 16 years and 9 months to pay off your $3,000, and you would have paid $3,090.42 in interest. At a *30%* interest rate, it would take 42 years for you to pay off this same debt, and you would have paid a whopping $13,459.02 toward interest!

Some companies are charging *35% interest* for customers they consider "high-risk." Individuals at high-risk include those trying to establish good credit after a past bankruptcy, those who stopped paying bills after losing a job, immigrants who haven't established credit records to qualify for better rates, and college students who got carried away with their first credit cards.

There is a common misconception that it is easy to transfer high interest credit card debt to a low interest credit card. Typically, individuals considered high-risk by credit card companies do not qualify for low interest credit cards. Low interest rates are reserved for consumers with good credit habits.

Here are some basic rules for developing good credit habits.

- Do not carry more than 2 credit cards. If you qualify for a credit card with a lower interest rate, pay off any higher interest rate cards and then close them out.

- When you switch cards, close out the old one and request they report to major credit bureaus that the account has been closed.. Too many open credit card accounts may make it difficult to get a new card.

- Buy only what you can afford. Make it a habit to use your debit card from your bank instead of a credit card.

- *Remember to pay your bills on time,* as late payments can affect your credit rating.

It is a wise idea to create a list of your credit card account numbers and credit company telephone numbers. If your credit cards are lost or stolen, it will be easier for you to contact all of the companies. If your credit cards are stolen, you should:

- File a police report immediately in the jurisdiction where the cards were stolen.

- Call the special numbers at the three national credit organizations immediately and have a fraud alert noted on your account

    Equifax 1-800-525-6285
    Experian (formerly TRW) 1-888-397-3742
    TransUnion 1-800-680-7289

- Call the Social Security Administration fraud line 1-800-269-0271 to place a fraud alert on your name.

INSURANCE – A NECESSARY EVIL

Our financial plan must take all aspects of life into consideration, including the protection of assets. Insurance is often referred to as "one of life's necessary evils." However, insurance serves as "preventive medicine" for your finances, and can save your life's work and investments in the event of an accident, disease, or other tragedy.

Good financial planning includes saving for short-term medical emergencies as well as long-term care. Short-term medical emergencies and long-term disabilities can derail well-planned financial health. Medical expenses can add up over time and become another financial stress point – *substantial debt.*

You may be an investment wiz but end up derailed by life's unexpected challenges if you fail to include insurance in your financial planning. The right insurance can help protect your savings, or allow you the ability to save. Let's review some insurance options:

Healthcare Insurance

A big factor that may impact your financial health is the failure to purchase health insurance. Although it may seem like you are saving when you choose not to pay the health insurance premiums, not having health insurance can be devastating to your physical and financial health. Even those women in the US who have health insurance, forgo routine preventive care and/or delay addressing a medical problem due to high deductibles.

There are many reasons people don't have health insurance, but what is clear is the impact this has on your health and finances. Numerous studies have demonstrated that not having health insurance can lead to limited access to the healthcare system. Those without insurance suffer from greater occurrences of heart disease, diabetes and other diseases. "As long as we have health benefits that are tied to employment status, then the access to health benefits is going to be problematic for certain groups," said Lisa Cubbings, lead author of a study and a researcher at Seattle's Battelle Memorial Research Institute, a non-profit organization.

The fear of losing their health insurance forces some people to remain in undesirable jobs or relationships, leading to added stress, subsequent physical problems, and the possibility of increased need for medications they're already taking.

Self-employed people often do not have sufficient knowledge about health insurance options, and may only think about it when an emergency arises. Risk-takers balance the gamble that they will not get sick against the savings in premiums not paid.

According to a 2001 report by the Kaiser Family Foundation,

22% of Californians are uninsured, compared to 17% in the entire US. A person's ability to afford health insurance largely depends on being employed by a company that offers it. The capability of employers to provide health coverage varies with economic trends. Spurred by several years of economic growth and strong demand for labor, 60% of employers offered health insurance benefits in 2001, compared to 48% in 1999. The national average was 67% in 2000, up from 61% in 1999. In some cases, employers hold off until a tight labor market forces them to offer health insurance, usually when the economy slows down. Only 29% of California employers offer health benefit to employees, compared to a national average of 37%.

Numerous studies have demonstrated that not having health insurance can lead to limited access to the healthcare system. Access to health insurance includes factors such as the size of the business and the race, ethnicity, gender of employees. According to a study published in the March 2001 issue of the *Journal of Health and Social Behavior*, America's racial and ethnic minorities are less likely to be insured than other employees, and the gap is widening.

One final note: Prior to trying to start a family, make sure you have health insurance that covers pregnancy and its complications. Few factors, if any, will have a greater impact than covering the cost of prenatal, delivery, and post-natal care.

Private Health Insurance

About 15.8 million Americans must purchase their own health insurance because they are self-employed or between jobs. We often hear about 50-year-olds paying monthly premiums of up to $300 for a single person, and up to $800 a month for a family of four.

Many good health insurance policies are available. Choosing wisely can save you a bundle. Your specific health insurance needs vary with your family's circumstances. If you have young children, you may choose coverage that provides preventive care and immunizations, as well as providing in the event of illness. If you are young, healthy, and have no children or dependants, you may opt for a policy with a high deductible to cover unexpected catastrophes. A deductible is the amount of money you are required to pay before your insurance will pay. The higher the deductible, the lower the premiums.

You should be aware that some insurance policies have a lifetime cap, which means that you do not have unlimited covered expenses. All of us are aware of the terrible tragedy suffered by Christopher Reeves. It is not common knowledge that his health insurance had a lifetime cap of only $1 million.

Health Maintenance Organizations (HMOs)

An HMO is a common type of group coverage that may provide good care for less money than other types of health insurance. The downside is that your choice of doctors, hospitals, and access to specialists is limited. Most employers now offer this type of insurance in order to save money. Health care is provided through physician networks. Patients in an HMO pay a co-pay for each office visit, which ranges from $5 to $40 or more, but you do not have to worry about meeting a deductible requirement.

You should be aware that HMOs can be a good deal if you are healthy, but may be a bad deal if you become very ill. Regardless of your specific health problem, you must first see a primary care provider for treatment or referral to a specialist. There may be restrictions on specialists, as the HMO prefers that you stay in the physician network. HMO physicians may be penalized financially if they refer you to a specialist. In some cases, you may have to pay for the specialist's care. And, if you suffer additional health problems because you were not seen or referred on time, you may not be able to sue the HMO, even in cases of major malpractice.

I have many patients who pay out of pocket to see me. But I encourage my patients to keep their HMOs because of the savings benefit and coverage provided in the event of major health problems.

Preferred Provider Organizations (PPOs)

A PPO is more expensive than an HMO, but offers more choices. This may be the best option for individuals who want to choose their healthcare provider. You still have to see a healthcare provider within their network. If you see a provider out of the network, only 60% to 70% of your costs will be covered, compared to 80% if you see a provider in the network. Most PPOs do not have a "gatekeeper" – meaning you do not need a referral to see a specialist.

Indemnity Policies

These plans are the most expensive and exist for those who want the ability to choose their physicians and hospitals. One way to reduce the monthly premium in these plans is to select a very high deductible.

"Any Doctor" Policies

These plans are less expensive than indemnity policies, but more expensive than PPOs. They are like PPOs, but there is no limited physician network, so you can see any healthcare provider you wish or go to any hospital of your choice.

POS

These plans are run by HMOs and are similar to a PPO. This insurance will pick up most, if not all, charges incurred if you have to see a specialist outside the HMO network providers.

Medical Savings Accounts (MSAs)

The Health Insurance Portability and Accountability Act (HIPAA) went into effect January 1, 1997, and created an ideal way to pay for healthcare and save money. MSAs are individual trust accounts set up specifically for the purpose of paying medical expenses. Current law places a cap of $750,000 on these policies. MSAs must be covered by a qualified health insurance plan and are limited to people under the age of 65, individuals, employees in small businesses (50 or fewer employees), and the self-employed. By law, the minimum MSA policy deductible is $3,000 for a single person and $4,500 for a family.

An MSA qualified plan usually costs less than a standard insurance plan. MSAs are tax-deductible, are allowed to earn income on a tax-deferred basis, and may be used to pay for medical expenses such as minor and routine medical expenses, dental, vision, hearing, mental health, prescription drugs, eyeglasses, and hearing aids. MSAs may also be used to pay for alternative services, such as chiropractic treatments, acupuncture, and other "qualified" healthcare and health insurance expenses as defined by the Internal Revenue Service. There are no restrictions on choice of healthcare provider or limitations on pharmacy services. Any unused money can be invested and accumulate interest tax-free. You can use these excess funds to pay for long-term care premiums, to cover Medicare deductibles, and to pay for Medicare supplemental coverage.

Medical Savings Accounts offer advantages that include:

- They can be used for qualified medical expenses tax-free for life.
- Contributions are 100% tax-deductible in the year they are made.
- The contributions grow tax deferred.
- The funds can be used to pay COBRA or other medical premiums during periods of unemployment or temporary layoff.
- Unused money can be withdrawn at age 65 for non-medical reasons without penalty.

Cafeteria Plans

With this type of insurance, your employer allots you a set dollar amount annually to spend on health benefits. These benefits may include vision-care plans, drug plans, dental plans and healthcare.

Defined Contribution

With this type of plan, your employer typically pays the first $2,000 toward your healthcare costs for the year. You are responsible for the next $2,000. Your employer purchases a lower cost, catastrophic insurance plan with a high deductible. Catastrophic insurance will cover anything above $4,000.

Concierge or Boutique Medical Practices

For the affluent who do not worry about cost and desire very personalized care, this is the way to go. This insurance, offered by physicians, carries an annual fee of several thousand dollars. In return, you have access to such services as immediate access to a physician, home visits, assistance with medical decisions, and the ability to have your physician accompany you to a specialist's office.

HOW TO CHOOSE THE BEST POLICY FOR YOU

Before you begin shopping for medical coverage, figure out what type of plan fits your needs and how much you can afford.

- Check with:

  - Your auto or homeowner's insurance agent.
  - Your financial planner.
  - A professional or trade group, or college alumni association.
  - The Internet. Regardless of your age, you can find reliable information under managed care options at the AARP www.aarp.org/hcchoices/options/pick.html.

- Your state insurance department, which is responsible for licensing and regulating insurance companies doing business in your state. They often have consumer information and can help with complaints. www.naic.org/1regulator/usamap.htm.

- When you decide on a plan, be sure to ask about:

  - Coverage limitations – maternity, mental, and drug coverage.
  - Which hospital(s) you have access to in your area.
  - Pre-existing condition coverage - If you have a pre-existing condition, such as breast cancer or heart disease, you may have difficulty finding a company willing to sell you a policy. Some companies may agree to sell you a policy, but will exclude coverage for that particular condition. About 25% of pregnancies are unintended. Pregnancy without maternity coverage is considered a pre-existing condition in many cases.
  - Rate increases.
  - Lifetime benefit limits. Consider supplemental insurance to cover health costs over and above the lifetime benefit.

Many life situations can cause you to lose your health coverage. These include the loss of your employer-sponsored health plan due to the death of your spouse, divorce or separation, a reduction in the number of hours worked, or simply quitting your job.

OTHER TYPES OF HEALTH INSURANCE

Medicare

Medicare is a health insurance program for people who are blind, disabled, or 65 years of age and older. Individuals with end-stage renal disease (permanent kidney failure treated with dialysis or transplant) are also eligible.

Medicaid (*Medi-Cal* in California)

This is a program created by the federal government to provide basic health and long-term care for low-income Americans. Children, pregnant women, families, the elderly, blind and the permanently disabled are eligible, but eligibility criteria may differ from state to state.

County Medical Services (CMS)

This is a county program that covers health benefits for low-income adults who do not qualify for either Medicaid or Medicare.

SAVING MONEY ON PRESCRIPTION DRUGS

The lack of prescription drug coverage translates into high out-of-pocket expenses for all, especially for seniors on a limited budget. Medicare offers limited drug coverage. Women are more likely to have lower incomes, to live longer, and to suffer from chronic disease, and end up spending substantially more for prescription drugs than men.

According to the AARP, while nearly 26 million people in the US have prescription drug coverage through their health insurance policy, approximately 14 million Americans are not covered and are forced to pay for all of their prescription drugs. The average annual out-of-pocket cost for prescription drugs with a drug coverage plan in place is $320, translating to an annual savings of $270.

A simple illness can be very costly. Co-payments for prescription drugs can also be expensive. The last time my niece, Kisha, went to the doctor for a sore throat my sister paid a $30 co-pay for the visit. At the pharmacy, she was offered the choice of paying $30 for a brand name medication or $20 for a generic. If Marise had not had health insurance, the visit to the doctor's office would have been $60 or more and the medications would have cost more than the drug co-pay. The remaining alternative for many is to suffer with the illness and receive no health care at all.

Here are some tips that may help you save money on prescription drug costs:

- During your annual physical, ask your healthcare provider whether over-the-counter or generic drugs are appropriate for you.
- If possible, buy your medicine in bulk. A 30-day supply of generic drugs may cost $5, while a 90-day supply costs $10. The cost of a 30-day supply of brand name medication may be $15, while a 90-day supply costs $25. Your savings may be substantial, especially when multiple drugs are needed.
- Some drugs may cost the same for different dosages. In that case, double the dose and divide it at home with a pill splitter. Check with your doctor or pharmacist before doing this because it is not appropriate for all drugs.
- Shop around for drugs that you have to take long-term. Local pharmacies and online or mail-order pharmacies may be willing to match the lowest prices from other sources.

🌱🌱

Healthcare Legalities

There are two important forms that need to be completed to ensure that your wishes concerning the care you receive are carried out in the event you are unable to make decisions yourself. These forms are a *living will* and a *durable power of attorney for healthcare.*

In a living will, you need to express the kind of medical care you want under the circumstances you describe. In my living will, I wrote, "I do not want to be kept alive with any kind of artificial means, such as a respirator or a feeding tube."

A durable power of attorney for healthcare, or a "healthcare proxy," addresses your wishes for healthcare decisions and designates the specific person who is responsible for making your decisions. Consult an attorney concerning applicable laws in your state prior to drawing up either of these forms.

Part of disability planning includes naming the person responsible for managing your assets if you should become incapacitated. This can be accomplished through a regular power of attorney.

DENTAL COVERAGE

According to the National Association of Dental Plans, only 55% of Americans have dental benefits of any sort. About 87% of large employers offer employees some type of dental plan.

There are several types of dental plans: indemnity plans, dental HMOs, and PPOs. The limitations and cost of each type of plan differ similar to health insurance. If you are young and healthy, you may decide not to purchase dental insurance; this is fine as long as you can afford to pay for bi-annual cleanings and the occasional filling. If you do not have dental insurance, a cracked tooth or crown that needs to be replaced can take a big bite out of your budget. A crown can cost as much as $800, and much more if you need a root canal. I strongly recommend that you shop around before deciding on the best dental plan for you and your family.

DISABILITY COVERAGE

Disability coverage is often overlooked, even though being unemployed due to disability for an extended period of time can have a disastrous financial impact. In addition to your regular living expenses, you now have the added cost of medical expenses. *Statistics demonstrate that we are more likely to become disabled during our prime working years than we are to die.* One in 5 people between the ages of 35 and 65 will become disabled, and 1 out of 7 will be disabled for at least five years before reaching age 65. Only 40% of Americans have disability insurance compared to 70% with life insurance.

Disability insurance may be offered through your employer or you may have to purchase it independently. An agent can advise you, but a guideline is to purchase disability coverage to replace approximately 60% of your current income. Some state laws require employers to deduct a portion of your salary for State Disability Insurance. Self-employed individuals should also purchase disability insurance. Be aware that there is a waiting period of 30 to 90 days before coverage begins; longer waiting periods will reduce your cost.

If you purchase your own disability insurance, be sure to do so with after-tax dollars so any benefit paid to you is not taxable. Consider buying from a no-load insurance company for a potential savings of 10% to 30%, dependent upon your age. Purchase a policy that's guaranteed renewable or non-cancelable. You may be able to save money by declining cost-of-living increases.

🌱🌿

LONG-TERM CARE INSURANCE COVERAGE

Another overlooked health "safety net" is long-term care insurance. As our population ages and healthcare costs escalate, adult children are becoming increasingly concerned about caring for their aging parents, and with how they themselves will be cared for in their old age. Many families are already dealing with the challenges of mental or physical disability, or prolonged illness. For thousands of others, these realities may be just around the corner. The challenge is to provide the best possible long-term care without imposing financial and emotional hardship on the rest of the family.

In most cases, families must plan for long-term care without answers to key questions:

- Will round-the-clock nursing home care or assistance with activities of daily living be necessary?
- Will home healthcare be sufficient?
- Will Medicare pay for it?
- Does the patient qualify for Medicaid?
- What costs will the family incur?

In the absence of long-term care insurance, family members may provide the necessary care in lieu of paying a healthcare professional; however, this can create significant stress for the parent, the child and other family members. A study commissioned by the GE Center for Financial Learning in November of 2000, revealed that 70% of baby boomers felt they were responsible for paying for their own long-term care, but only 7% had purchased long-term care insurance. According to this study, the primary reason for not purchasing long-term care insurance coverage was *cost*.

How much long-term care insurance costs depends on a number of factors, such as the amount of coverage (usually expressed as the daily benefit), how many years you will be able to receive that benefit, the elimination period (the period of time before any benefits will be paid), and your health status. The younger you are when you purchase the policy, the lower your annual premiums are likely to be.

Government assistance programs offer limited help. Medicare provides limited long-term care benefits and may require substantial co-payments. Medicaid has strict financial eligibility criteria and generally requires beneficiaries to deplete their savings, or "spend down" before paying for services. Other public services may be available but may be offered on a sliding-fee scale, based on ability to pay. And, there may be long waiting lists.

Long-term care insurance, like other types of health insurance mentioned, can provide security and help to reduce stress, which may *cause* illness. Are you beginning to see the connection?

🌱🌱🌱

UMBRELLA COVERAGE

Umbrella coverage is an addition to your homeowner's policy that protects you against damage suits such as mental anguish, physical injury, sickness or disease, libel, slander, wrongful entry or eviction. At least $1 million worth is a must in these litigating times. The average cost of such a policy is $200 a year.

🌱🌱🌱

206 MIND, BODY, SOUL & MONEY

INSURANCE PREMIUM SAVINGS

By simply increasing the deductible on your health, homeowner's, or automobile insurance, from $250 to $500, you may reduce your premiums by more than 10%. Check with your insurance auto, homeowner's, or renter's insurance company to see if you may receive a substantial discount by insuring both home and auto with the same company. And, be sure to ask about other available discounts.

LIFE INSURANCE

A life insurance policy pays a death benefit, upon the death of the insured, to the person(s) named in the policy as the beneficiary. You need life insurance if you have a spouse, parents, siblings, or children who depend on you for their support. How much insurance you need depends, in part, on the length of time these individuals will need your continued support after your death. In order to estimate the death benefit you need to purchase, you need to know the annual expenses of your dependants. You then need to purchase $100 in coverage for each $5,000 in annual expenses. You may wish to discuss this with an insurance agent prior to purchasing a policy.

It is not generally recommended that you purchase life insurance on your children. You are far more likely to die before they do. Save the money you would have spent on monthly premiums and instead use it for their education, to reduce your debt, or to purchase additional life insurance on yourself or your spouse.

WORKING WITH A FINANCIAL ADVISOR

Hiring a financial advisor does not mean that all financial responsibilities are delegated to that person. This relationship is similar to your relationship with your doctor. You need to understand any health problems and not blindly accept proposed treatments in life-and-death situations.

Just as you are ultimately responsible for your personal health, you are responsible for your financial health and well-being. I strongly suggest that you seek the help of a licensed financial advisor. Look for a financial advisor who can help you to identify appropriate investment goals and strategies for you. If you decide not to hire a financial advisor, a periodic financial check-up is recommended.

Choosing a Financial Advisor

First, you need to decide the extent of service you wish to be provided. Some options include:

- Execution of investment trades *(a broker)*. If this is desired, you may also require the services of a:
- full-service broker (research and suggestion on securities)
- discount broker (execution of trades only)
- Provide comprehensive and continuous investment advice *(an investment advisor)*. If this is desired, you need to decide how the advisor will be compensated for his/her services:
- commissions generated on products sold, or
- an asset-based fee based on the value of the portfolio.

In either case, you need to decide whether your advisor:

- has *discretion* to make all investment decisions without prior approval by you, or
- is *non-discretionary* and must obtain prior approval from you for all investment decisions.

Additional Notes on Choosing a Financial Advisor

It is important to do a background check on the person you select as your financial advisor. Here are some things to look for:

Education - A college degree is not required to become a broker and/ or investment advisor; however, given the degree of sophistication of investment products and services, it is highly recommended that the advisor have a four-year college degree.

Training - There are a number of certification courses for brokers and investment advisors. The more recognized designations are:

CFA – Charted Financial Analyst (www.aimr.org)

CFP – Certified Financial Planner (www.cfp-board.org)

ChFC – Chartered Financial Counselor ww.amercoll.edu)

CIMA – Certified Investment Management Analyst (www.imca.org)

CIMC – Chartered Investment Management Consultant (www.icimc.org)

PFS – Personal Financial Specialist (www.aicpa.org)

Experience – As with any profession, there is a strong relationship between years of experience and professional knowledge; however, "experience" should be further qualified by the number of years the professional has spent handling clients similar to you.

Regulatory authorities have not defined practices that constitute "investment advice." Therefore, you need to confirm that the professional will provide the following services:

- An analysis of your investment goals, objectives, and cash flow requirements.
- An asset allocation study that specifically addresses you risk and return profile.
- A written investment statement outlining your investment strategy.
- Access to screened mutual funds and/or money managers appropriate for your plan.
- Quarterly reports that shows the performance of your portfolio.
- A breakdown of all fees and expenses associated with the management of your account.

Internet resources:

- GE's Center for Financial Learning
  (www.financiallearning.com)
- Securities and Exchange Commission (SEC) (www.sec.gov)
- Information on SEC Registered Investment Advisors
  (www.adviserinfo.sec.gov/IAPD/Content/Search)
- Information on Registered Representatives (brokers)
  (www.nasaa.org)

A Word of Caution

You cannot afford to be complacent when it comes to your relationship with your money or your financial advisor. It is your obligation to stay up-to-date and to make sure that your questions are answered to your satisfaction. If at any time you are not satisfied with any aspect of the relationship, it is time to look for another advisor.

ESTATE PLANNING

Estate planning consists of the preparation of a plan to administer and dispose of your property before or after your death, and may include a will, trusts, gifts, or powers of attorney. If no estate plan is in place, your heirs may be forced to pay estate taxes as high as 40% or more. *Your financial plan is incomplete without a will or trust in place.* Your advisor can help you to decide the best approach to take.

CONCLUDING THOUGHTS ON FINANCIAL HEALTH

I am very concerned about your "financial "fitness" because it directly affects your physical and mental health. Setting long-term financial goals, paying off debt, and beginning to save, may ease overall stress in your life and prevent avoidable health problems. Feeling that you are in control of your finances is truly empowering. Keys to prosperity and financial health include monitoring spending, building cash savings, reducing high-interest debt, and having proper insurance. I agree with Thomas Stanley & William Danko, authors of *The Millionaire Next Door:* "Financially independent people seem to be better able to visualize the future benefits of defining their goals."

If you've read through this long chapter and are yawning, here's a eye-opening wake-up call in the form of a short reality-check questionnaire:

Wake-up Financial Questionnaire

1. Do you know your monthly cost of living?

   Yes No

2. Do you know if your home mortgage interest rate is competitive?

   Yes No

3. Do you know the interest rate on your credit cards?

   Yes No

4. Are your insurance premiums competitively priced?

   Yes No

5. Is your insurance coverage adequate?

   Yes No

6. Do you know how to consolidate your debt using your home equity?

   Yes No

7. Do you know your income tax bracket?

                                         Yes No

8. Do you have money to invest, but don't know where to start?

                                         Yes No

9. Is your stock portfolio balanced?

                                         Yes No

10. Do you have investment goals?

                                         Yes No

11. Do you have or plan to set aside money for your retirement?

                                         Yes No

12. Do you know about the advantages and differences of IRA, ROTH IRA, and KEOGH accounts?

                                         Yes No

13. Do you know the difference between tax deferred and tax exempt?

                                         Yes No

14. Are you getting motivated to save more than you spend?

                                         Yes No

Building a healthy "financial house" can take a lifetime. For "financial fitness," I encourage you to develop a financial plan and obtain help with money management. Some personal secrets to prosperity I have learned over the years:

- Money should not rule all decisions. Remaining in a job or relationship solely because of economic security is not worth the stress that comes with it.
- Don't eat the turkey today and the feathers tomorrow!
- Abundance is more than money.
- The wealthiest person on earth is the one who needs the least.
- Prosperity is also an activity of the soul.

Q AND A ON YOUR FINANCIAL HEALTH

Q: *How can I plan for tomorrow when it gives me a headache to try to pay for today?*
A: Create a budget. Determine what you actually spend each month. It is easy to keep track of large expenses such as mortgage and car payments. But the variable items such as food, clothing and entertainment are often what get away from us.

Q: *I know that when I worry a lot about my finances, I experience lower back pain. What types of exercises or activities do you suggest I participate in order to help relieve my stress?*
A: Put your finances in order, since research has documented a correlation between stress and lower back disorders. Relaxation exercises, yoga, walking, and massage help to relieve stress as well as helping with lower back pain.

Q: *I find the more I worry about my finances, the more I spend, which causes me more stress. How can I stop engaging in this compulsive spending behavior?*
A: You need to ask yourself why you need to spend money when you are under stress. Working with a therapist may help you to understand your behavior and overcome it.

Q: *Just getting started is difficult for me. Who do you suggest I talk to in order to get a solid financial plan in place?*

A: When I started my private practice, I owed more than $100,000 in student loans and start-up costs. I found a good financial planner who showed me how to pay off my debt and how to save for the future. I followed her advice and never regretted it.

Q: *It's difficult to step back and take stock of your situation when you're faced with the reality and stress of paying bills. What steps do you suggest I take in order to gain a clearer perspective of my situation so I don't worry myself sick?*
A: My financial planner had me list all of my monthly bills and living expenses on an expense sheet. I also listed my income. I could clearly see what was going on and I planned accordingly.

Q: *After a plan is developed, what happens next?*
A: The best plan is useless unless it is put into action. A CPA/PFS can advise you how to implement the plan and can put you in touch with other financial experts as needed.

Q: *How often should I update my financial plan?*
A: It is good to review the plan when there is a significant life event such as marriage, birth, death or divorce. Any change in financial position should be evaluated as well. An annual update should review how the plan is being implemented, plus any changing goals and circumstances.

Q: *What types of gynecological disorders can arise as a result of financial stress?*
A: Sometimes it may be difficult to correlate gynecological symptoms with financial stress. In my experience, when a healthy woman shows symptoms such as irregular bleeding, vaginal dryness, low sex drive, or increased hot flashes when she is already on hormone replacement therapy, a little probing in many cases reveals stress as an underlying issue.

Q: *So often I am confused by the amount of financial debt I owe that it causes me to become depressed. How can I better prepare myself financially so I don't become so overwhelmed?*
A: You have to act, or else high interest rates will increase your debt in a short period of time. Working with a financial advisor is a good idea. There are also counselors that can teach you debt consolidation as well as ways to avoid repeating the situation.

Q: *You suggest three types of health insurance that are helpful to our physical and financial health. What other types of health insurance should I consider to lessen the impact on my health and finances?*
A: The fourth overlooked health "safety-net" is long-term care insurance.

Q: *I would have to consider myself a risk-taker when it comes to health insurance. I am currently self-employed and have opted not to purchase health insurance because it's very expensive. What types of affordable health insurance options are there for the self-employed?*
A: You should not be without health insurance! You should consult with an insurance advisor to learn about affordable health insurance options. My husband and I are both healthy and self-employed. We chose health insurance with a high deductible in order to reduce our premiums. You may also be eligible to join a group plan to reduce premiums.

Q: *What does disability insurance cover that health insurance does not?*
A: Disability insurance provides a partial replacement of earnings to an employee who is unable to work during short periods of total disability (short-term disability) and long periods of total or partial disability (long-term disability). Health insurance covers the cost of medical care.

Q: *As a precaution, I purchased disability insurance through my employer. If I left work due to disability, how long would I receive payments under a typical disability insurance policy? Six months? One year? More than one year?*
A: Short Term Disability is intended to replace a portion of lost income for a period of 13 to 52 weeks. The Age Discrimination in Employment Act (ADEA) mandates long-term disability coverage until age 70. Under some standard plans, if an employee is disabled prior to age 60, the maximum duration of benefits extends to age 65, or normal Social Security retirement age. If an employee is disabled between age 60 and 70, benefits will be payable for 1 to 5 years, depending on the age at disability.

Q: *Would disability insurance cover my family if they become disabled?*
A: Disability insurance is a benefit available to the employee only.

Q: *Are there services that long-term care does not cover that I need to be aware of?*
A: A long-term care policy is intended to provide reimbursement for covered long-term care expenses when needed. Most long-term care policies sold today are comprehensive policies and cover a wide range of services. Understand the terms of the policy prior to purchase.

Q: *What are the qualifications for Medicaid?*
A: While specific qualifications vary from state to state, you should be aware that Medicaid does not provide coverage unless the individual is impoverished, and generally, in a nursing home (The New York Times, 7/26/99). Contact the authorities in your state for specifics.

Q: *How great is my risk if I don't purchase long-term care insurance now?*
A: This is a personal decision and will differ based on your disposable assets, risk tolerance, and the cost/ benefit outcome of long-term care insurance. Even the very wealthy need to evaluate the cost and potential benefits of long-term care insurance before risking their life savings. The United Seniors Health Council, a nonprofit consumer organization devoted to the issues of the elderly, maintains that long term care insurance is appropriate if it costs no more than 7% of your retirement income and: 1) you have assets of $75,000 or more per person, excluding home and car; 2) your retirement income is at least $35,000 per person per year; 3) you can pay the premiums without adversely affecting your lifestyle; and 4) you are financially able to afford future premiums that may increase by as much as 30%. (http://www.unitedseniorshealth.org/html/ltc_buyornot.html)

Q: *How should I plan for out-of-pocket expenses above and beyond what is typically covered in a long-term care insurance policy?*
A: In part, the answer depends on the type of long-term care insurance you choose, and the specifics of your policy. It also depends on your assets. Long-term care expenses can be substantial. The average cost of a year in a nursing home is almost $56,000 (Reuters, 12/13/00), and can be much higher in metropolitan areas (e.g., more than $100,000 in New York City according to The New York Times, 2/16/00). In-home care is less expensive, but still significant. Skilled in-home nursing care averages $105 a day, adult care is $60 per day, and home care averages $80 per visit (CNN Financial Network, 8/25/99).

Q: *What websites describe what Medicare will cover?*
A: http://www.medicare.gov is the official US Government site for Medicare information.

Q: *What is Medigap and how does it differ from Medicaid and Medicare?*
A: Medicare Supplement insurance (often called Medigap or MedSup) is private insurance that helps to cover the gaps in Medicare coverage. These gaps include hospital deductibles, deductibles for office visits, and coinsurance payments, what Medicare considers excess physician charges. They are not long-term care insurance policies [HIAA (Health Insurance Association of America), Guide to Long-Term Care Insurance, 1999]. Medicare has significant limitations with regard to long-term care. It pays for 20 days in a skilled nursing facility and part of the cost for the next 80 days, but only after a hospital stay of three days or more. Medicare does not pay for simple, long-term, custodial care (CBSMarketWatch.com, 11/2/00). Only individuals with negligible assets qualify for Medicaid (The Wall Street Journal, 3/31/99).

Q: *I have a family of my own and my parents do not have long-term care insurance. I just don't see how we can afford another insurance payment. What other long-term care alternatives do we have?*
A: Many local communities have a wide array of in-home supportive services that may allow your parents to stay in their home where they feel most comfortable and secure. I suggest that you learn more about the agencies in your community that provide meal delivery, in-home nursing care, assistance with chores and bathing, as well as other miscellaneous services. Church groups, local government organizations, and nonprofit organizations may offer these services; however, it is best to identify these organizations and understand the scope of services available before care is needed.

Q: *Is there an ideal age for people to purchase long-term care insurance? You mentioned that premiums are lower at younger ages. What's the break-even point?*
A: There are many things to consider. As you stated, long-term care premiums are generally much lower when purchased at a younger age, so the longer the purchase is delayed, the higher the premium is likely to be at the time of purchase. Bear in mind that a person may need long-term care at any age.

Actor Christopher Reeve was 42 when he was disabled as the result of an accident.

Q: *I'm 45 years old. Am I too young to buy long-term care insurance?*
A: There is no one answer that fits all situations. The best time to purchase a long-term care insurance policy is during your middle years, ages 45 to 59, when the premiums are lower. Keep in mind that every circumstance is different and you may want to discuss yours with a knowledgeable financial professional.

Q: *How do I go about starting to prepare a financial plan?*
A: Start by educating yourself. After you've learned more, work with a financial professional to build a plan that's right for you. Remember to revisit your plan as your life changes.

Q: *How do insurance companies determine how much long-term care insurance premiums will cost?*
A: Premiums depend on your age and amount of coverage purchased. Insurance companies use actuarial formulas to evaluate risk and policy benefits to determine appropriate premiums.

Q: *If my employer's health insurance is too expensive and doesn't cover much, are there private or independent insurance plans I can purchase?*
A: Generally, group health coverage through an employer is more affordable than individual coverage; however, you may be able to obtain more comprehensive benefits through individual coverage. Consult a health insurance professional for an explanation of coverage options and costs.

Q: *Can financial stress lead to physical ailments besides lower back pain? I constantly worry about my financial situation and I've developed a horrible allergy. Could these be related?*
A: Definitely! Allergies can result from stress. I recommend taking time for yourself, try some relaxation techniques, and work toward correcting your financial situation.

🌱

REFERENCES

Journal of Periodontology. *Financial Stress Doubles Periodontal Disease Risk*. July 19, 1999 from The American Academy of Periodontology

The Influence of Psychosocial Stress, Gender, and Personality on Mechanical Loading of the Lumbar Spine Marras WS, Davis KG, Heaney CA, Maronitis AB, Allread WG Spine. 2000

CIA World Factbook 2000. Published January 1, 2001.

Cubbins, Lisa A. *Economic Change and Health Benefits: Structural Trends in Employer-based Health Insurance*. Published March 2001, *Journal of Health and Social Behavior*

2000 Statistics for US Health Insurance Coverage. Published July 2001 by Agency for Healthcare Research and Quality, Rockville, MD.

Health Insurance Association of America. *Public Opinion: Disability Insurance*. September 2000

Foster, Ann C. Brief: Employee Benefits in the United States, *1994-95*. Published spring 1998, Vol. 3. No. 1, *Compensation and Working Conditions*.

Employees Participating Selected Benefits in United States, 1991-1992. Table 192, Published February 12, 1996.

Dr. Christopher Hayes, Center for Aging Research &Education (CARE) *STAT Survey (Secure Tomorrow's Autonomy Today*. November 2000 Published in GE Center for Financial Learning

US Commerce Department, *Spending Gains Continue*, August 28, 2000 http://cnnfn.cnn.com/2000/08/28/economy/economy

McDonough, Peggy. *Income Dynamics and Adult Mortality in the United States, 1972 through 1989*. Paper accepted April 1, 1997. Published in *American Journal of Public Health*, September 1, 1997

RESOURCES

150 Ways To Divorce Without Going Broke, an information-packed brochure by Ginita Wall.

150 Ways to Save Taxes Through Life's Transitions, by Ginita Wall, CPA, CFP™, with Jessica Richman

> To receive the above brochures, send $5.00 and a double-stamped self-addressed #10 long envelope to: WIFE, Dept DP, Box 910014, San Diego, CA 92191

Important Resource Websites:

www.drcarolle.com *(Please visit mine anytime!)*

www.financiallearning.com (GE's Center for Financial Learning)

www.blackenterprise.com

www.moneycentralmsn.com

www.ebri.org (Employee Benefit Research Institute)

www.wife.org (Women's Institute for Financial Education)

(Please note that since websites sometimes change on the Internet, do your research using a good meta-search engine such as http://www.google.com/)

RECOMMENDED BOOKS

Think & Grow Rich: A Black Choice, by Dennis Kimbro

The Truth About Money, by Ric Edelman

Pay Yourself First: A Guide to Financial Success, by Jesse B. Brown.

The Millionaire Next Door, by Thomas Stanley & William Danko

Simple Wisdom for Rich Living (Longstreet Press, $9.95), by Oseola McCarty

New Strategies for College Funding, by Raymond D. Loewe, CLU, DhFC and K. C. Dempster

Rich Dad, Poor Dad, by Robert T. Kiyosaki, with Sharon L. Lechter, C.P.A.

Love and Money: 150 Tips for Couples by Kathleen Gurney, Ph.D. and Ginita Wall, CPA, FP™, with Jessica Richman, CFS.

The Road to Wealth: A Comprehensive Guide to Your Money–Everything You Need to Know in Good and Bad Times, by Suze Orman

The Courage to Be Rich, by Suze Orman

🌱🌱

Monthly

BUDGET

Worksheet

MONTHLY BUDGET WORKSHEET

Description of Expense   What You Spend

HOUSEHOLD

Mortgage or Rent .... $_____

Utilities (gas/electric) .... $_____

Water/Sewer .... $_____

Trash removal .... $_____

Telephone (home and cell), pager .... $_____

TV cable/satellite .... $_____

Computer connection .... $_____

Banking Expenses .... $_____

Home maintenance & repair costs .... $_____

Housecleaning service/cleaning supplies .... $_____

Gardener/pool maintenance .... $_____

Computer-related expenses

(maintenance/supplies/upgrades) .... $_____

Child care .... $_____

School tuition .... $_____

Children's allowance .... $_____

P.O Box expense .... $_____

Postage .... $_____

Total Household Expenses ....$_____

CREDIT CARDS & DEBTS

Credit card payments .... $_____

Child support .... $_____

Alimony .... $_____

Student Loans .... $_____

Other Loans .... $_____

Total Debt Expenses ....$_____

TRANSPORTATION

Auto payment(s) .... $_____

Auto gas/oil .... $_____

Auto repair/washing/other .... $_____
Parking .... $_____
Other transportation (taxi/train/bus) .... $_____

       Total Transportation ....$_____

INSURANCE
Homeowners'/Renters' .... $_____
Auto .... $_____
Life .... $_____
Health/dental .... $_____
Disability/other .... $_____

       Total Insurance ....$_____

FOOD & MEDICINE
Groceries .... $_____
Kitchen/cooking supplies .... $_____
Special dietary needs/vitamins/supplements/
OTC drugs .... $_____
Pet food .... $_____
Prescription drugs .... $_____

       Total Food/Medicine ....$_____

PROFESSIONAL FEES
Doctors .... $_____
Dentist .... $_____
Eye care .... $_____
Attorney .... $_____
Veterinarian .... $_____

       Total Professional Fees ....$_____

ENTERTAINMENT & RECREATION

Eating out .... $_____

Movies .... $_____

Concerts/sporting events .... $_____

Videos (rental/purchase) .... $_____

Bad habits (cigarettes & alcohol) .... $_____

Gym membership .... $_____

Club/hobby dues/costs .... $_____

Books, magazines, newspaper .... $_____

Music (CD/tape purchase)...................................... $_____

Vacation & travel .... $_____

Gifts .... $_____

Other:_____ .... $_____

         Total Entertainment ....$_____

CLOTHING & ACCESSORIES

Purchases... $_____

Cleaning and repair .... $_____

         Total Clothing ....$_____

CONTRIBUTIONS

Religious.. $_____

Other charity... $_____

         Total Contributions ....$_____

PERSONAL ITEMS

Beauty treatments (hair/nails/massage) .... $_____

Cosmetic/Plastic Surgeries .... $_____

Personal care products .... $_____

(lotions, potions, shampoo)

Other:_____ .... $_____

         Total Personal Items ....$_____

TAXES, INVESTMENTS, SAVINGS

Accounting & tax preparations fees .... $_____

Federal taxes .... $_____

State taxes .... $_____

Local taxes .... $_____

Retirement Savings Plan Contribution .... $_____

Social Security taxes... $_____

Investments.. $_____

Total Taxes, Investments, Savings .... $_____

TOTAL MONTHLY EXPENDITURES* .... *$*_____

The following formula for working out the monthly amount for some expenditures takes a few steps for several reasons:

1. Some expenses will have to be an estimate based upon what you paid last year.

2. Some bills are paid yearly such as your auto license, homeowners'/renters' insurance or tax preparations fee. To get your monthly payment, **divide the total amount by 12**.

3. Some bills are paid every six months such as auto insurance, P.O Box. To get your monthly payment, **divide the total amount by 6.**

4. Some bills are paid every other week, such as housecleaning, gardening, **To find out the monthly payment, divide the amount by 2, then multiply by 52, then divide by 48, then multiply by 2 to get the *real* monthly amount.**

> I'll show you an example:
> Let's say you pay your gardener $50 per week. The formula works as follows: $50 ÷ 2 = $25 x 52 = $1,300 ÷ 48 = 54 x 2 = *$108*
> *Why?* If you pay your gardener on Saturdays, some months have 4 Saturdays, and some have 5. In the event there are 5 Saturdays, you may have to make 3 payments instead of 2. If you don't use this formula, you have written down $100 per month for gardening instead of the actual $108. In a year you would have been off $96! ($8 x 12 months = $96)

*NOTE: *You should put aside six months worth of your Total Monthly Expenditures as a cushion. Make sure you consider important life events, like retirement, job changes, college education and major purchases. Also consider the impact of a potential crisis, like a disability or job loss.*

MONTHLY INCOME

Wages or salary .... $_____
(**calculate if paid every other week)
Dividends (mutual funds, stocks, etc.)....................... $_____
Interest (CDs, savings account, etc.)........................ $_____
Other .... $_____

         TOTAL MONTHLY INCOME ....$_____

**On the plus side, if you get paid every other week (meaning every other Friday instead of the 1st and the 15th) you actually get paid *two extra pay checks per year*. To calculate your REAL monthly income do the following:

       Let's say that you receive a paycheck of $1000 every two weeks. Your annual income is actually $26,000. Most people assume that their annual income is $24,000, therefore, their monthly income is: $2,000. Instead, because there are 52 weeks in one year, your monthly income is $2,333.33 ($1,000 x [52 / 2 = 26] x 26 = 26,000 / 12)
       What happens is that twice a year you get an extra paycheck for $1,000. If you have difficulty saving throughout the year, you could just put that amount aside when you receive it.

Now figure your ***Monthly Net Cash Flow***, which is your Total Monthly Income less your Total Monthly Expenditures.

       Total Monthly Income $_____
       Total Monthly Expenditures $_____

          *MONTHLY NET CASH FLOW**** $_____

***Your Monthly Net Cash Flow determines how much you need to save each month to meet your financial goals. If your Monthly Net Cash Flow is positive it means that you have additional money available for saving and investing. If the figure is negative, you need to find ways to trim your monthly expenses!

Conclusion

Optimum health can thrive only when we are in a state of balance. We evolve and change as long as we are alive, and who we become is the result of how we develop and balance our mental, physical, spiritual and financial abilities.

Helping you to put your life in balance is my motivation for writing this book. It is the same motivation I have as a holistic healer who cares for the whole person, not just the body. I hope I've succeeded in showing you that good health means much more than having a healthy body.

I want your **mind** to have more control so you make better decisions. I want your **body** to have less stress, heal from illness, and have more energy. I want your **soul** to find peace and love enough to spread it around. I want you to manage your **money** better, have a workable budget, improve your standard of living, and protect your future.

If I could wave a magic wand and make it all happen, I would do it, *but it's up to you.* Love yourself enough to make some good, healthy changes, before something like panic attacks force you to change.

A few final thoughts:

· Commit to taking charge of your health today, as your body is the vehicle for your mind and the temple of your soul.

· You are creating who you are every day. However you visualize yourself, so you will become.

- We are living in a time of the most far-reaching and rapid changes in human history. Educate yourself – seek new information from the most credible and trust-worthy sources.

- Become more proactive about your relationship with money, savings and insurance.

- Anxiety blocks the flow of your own personal energy and fear blocks the flow of creativity. Take control of anxiety and fear by adjusting your attitude – be willing to change – be flexible. If it is overwhelming in any area, *seek professional help.*

- Put your energy into work and activities you value, for your self-esteem.

- When you live with a feeling of love for others, you live a much deeper life. When you live with a feeling of love for yourself, you live a less stressful life.

- Find a healthcare provider with whom you can create a great lasting relationship, even if you have to pay out-of-pocket.

- Keep in touch by checking my website www.drcarolle.com – and watch for my next book!

Afterword

I was talking to Charlotte Quiroga, CEO of the Sycuan Medical & Dental Clinic one day, when I casually mentioned that I was fed up with the "system" and would quit medicine altogether. "You are the best doctor I have ever met," she said looking at me in shock. "You cannot quit!" Charlotte and I had come a long way together. For many years we had worked together at the Southern Indian Health Clinic in San Diego County, where I headed a comprehensive peri-natal program. "What would it take for you to continue to practice medicine?" she asked, when she realized how *serious* I was.

"I want a place where I can take as much time as I want to see my patients, on a part-time basis, and get paid for it." "You got it, Dr Jean-Murat," she said. "You can come to my clinic. You decide how long you want to spend with the patients. I feel honored to have a physician like you who is not willing to compromise."

I started to work at the Sycuan clinic in July, 2001. It is situated on one of the many Native American reservations in San Diego County. Most of my patients were elated to find out that I did not quit after all. They did not mind waiting a long time to make an appointment, and then driving a long way to see me at the reservation. They liked the idea that they could continue to have the personalized, unhurried holistic care that I always gave them. And I liked the part-time practice arrangement so that I could work on my *Angels for Haiti* nonprofit foundation, and the other healthcare projects on my dream list…

In October, 2001 another unexpected path appeared for me. I was approached to become the medical director of a new Wellness Center for Midlife Women at Alvarado Hospital in San Diego, California – to create a unique center where the *special needs of midlife women* will be met, with all services provided "one-stop shopping" at the center or within walking distance.

This center for women is much needed.

Our world has become increasingly complicated and confusing, stretching our capacity to cope with the multitude of "stressors" brought on by fear, family, work, societal expectations and demands, finances, and the physical/mental changes of menopause. *The current health-care system with its "managed emphasis" does not adequately address the midlife needs of the 78 million people born from 1946 to 1964 in the US alone.*

These millions of baby boomers will set health-care standards for decades to come – They have more money than their parents did, they pro-actively seek a higher and healthier quality of life, and they refuse to grow old. As members of this group turn 50 they are as likely to seek *preventive education* and *health assessments* as they are to seek *treatment*. The Wellness Center for Midlife Women at Alvarado Hospital will provide all these important services in one beautiful place.

It's being built – maybe I will see you there someday!

🌱

Glossary

A

accounts receivable: money that is owed to a company for products or services that were sold on credit.

American Stock Exchange (AMEX): the second largest national stock exchange in the US, where primarily securities of small to mid-size companies are bought and sold. Options on many NYSE stocks are also traded on the AMEX.

amino acid: organic compound of carbon, hydrogen, oxygen, and nitrogen; the "building blocks" of protein.

amortization: an accounting term that refers to the reduction in the value of an intangible item, such as a patent or trademark, through periodic reductions in income.

anniversary date: the annual recurrence of an insurance policy's effective date. The anniversary date is often the time the owner of a universal life policy is permitted to make changes to the policy, such as increasing the death benefit.

annual report: the formal financial statement that a corporation issues annually to its shareholders.

annual return: the percentage increase in the value of an investment over a 12-month period or a series of 12-month periods, taking into account compounding of investment dividends or capital gains.

annuitant: the individual who is entitled to receive the benefits of an annuity.

annuity: regular payments to an individual according to a contract, for a specified or an indefinite time period.

anti-depressant: medication or process used to avoid depressive states.

antioxidant: a substance that prevents oxidation or inhibits reactions promoted by oxygen.

arteriosclerosis: used interchangeably with the term *atherosclerosis* to describe a condition affecting the arteries.

asset: any item of economic value owned by an individual or corporation.

asset allocation: the process of dividing investor funds among several classes of assets to limit risk and increase opportunities for gains.

atherosclerosis: a variety of conditions where there is thickening, hardening, and/or loss of elasticity of the artery walls, resulting in altered function of tissues and organs.

B

bacteria: microscopic organisms that can cause an infectious process, and that can be cured with antibiotics.

balance sheet: accounting statement that shows the amount of assets, liabilities, and owner's equity on a certain date.

barrier method: a birth control method like the diaphragm and condom that blocks entry of sperm into the cervix, uterus, and fallopian tubes.

basal metabolic rate (BMR): temperature of the body at the time of awakening.

bear: a person who believes that stock prices will fall. (Bear market = stock prices decreasing)

beneficiary: The party who will receive the death benefit of the contract (will) upon the insured' s death.

benign: non-cancerous.

beta carotene: compound in plants that the body converts into vitamin A.

birth control: any method used to prevent pregnancy, also known as contraception.

blood pressure: a measurement of the force applied against the walls of the arteries as the heart pumps blood through the body. The pressure is determined by the force and amount of blood pumped and the size and flexibility of the arteries." A reading consists of two numbers, for example: 112/77, which is read as "112 over 77."
The first number, *systolic blood pressure*, measures the maximum pressure exerted as the

heart contracts, while the lower number indicates *diastolic pressure*, a measurement taken between beats, when the heart is at rest.

According to high blood pressure guidelines from the American Heart Association (AHA), numbers under 140/90 and over 90/60 are generally considered normal in adults.

blue chips: the high-quality stocks of major corporations with long records of uninterrupted earnings and dividends, capable management, and good growth prospects.

book value: an indicator of a company's value, calculated by subtracting the company's liabilities from its total assets.

broker: an agent who executes buy and sell orders for securities or commodities for a fee.

bull: a person who believes that stock prices will rise. (Bull market = stock prices rising)

C

calories: the measure of the energies supplied by the food we eat. 1,600 calories = one pound of weight gain.

capital appreciation: the increase in a fund share's value.

capital gain (loss): profit (loss) from the sale of securities or other capital assets.

carbohydrates: chemical compounds found in plants, which includes all sugars, starches, and cellulose; a basic source of human energy.

carcinogens: cancer-producing agents.

cardiovascular disease: a general grouping of diseases of the heart and blood vessels.

cash surrender value: the value you receive upon termination of a permanent life insurance policy for any reason other than death of the insured.

cash value: the "savings" element of all permanent forms of life insurance. The cash value is the amount of money a policy owner can get for surrendering the policy

cash value of life insurance: the amount of money accumulated in a whole life, universal life or a variable life insurance policy. The cash value is accumulated based on the return of the underlying investments in the policy.

Certificates of Deposit (CDs): FDIC-insured account offered by banks and savings and loans.

commission: a fee an investor pays a broker for buying or selling securities.

cervix: the neck-like narrow end of the uterus that opens into the vagina; it stretches to allow a baby to be born.

Caesarean section (C-section): surgically assisted birth that requires cutting of the mother's abdomen and uterus so the baby can be removed.

chlamydia: a bacterial infection of the pelvic organs and urinary tract transmitted by sexual activity.

colorectal: related to the colon (portion of large bowels) and the rectum.

colposcope: instrument used to visually examine the vagina and the cervix.

conception: fertilization of the egg by the sperm.

condom, female: a polyurethane sheet that covers the cervix and lines the walls of the vagina to prevent pregnancy.

condom, male: a covering of thin latex (rubber) or animal intestines put on the penis before sex to help prevent pregnancy and the spread of sexually transmitted disease (STD).

Consumer Price Index (CPI): a measure of the change in prices of a fixed basket of goods and services, including food, clothing, medical care, transportation, housing and electricity.

current market value: the largest amount any buyer is currently willing to pay for an asset.

cyst: a sac of fluid that develops abnormally within a cavity or organ of the body.

D

death benefit: the amount of money paid to the beneficiary when the insured dies.

debt: obligations in the form of bonds, loans, notes or mortgages, owed to another person or institution and required to be paid by a specified date.

depreciation: an accounting term that refers to the reduction in the value of physical assets through periodic reductions in income.

diabetes: disease caused by failure of the body to produce insulin or to use insulin efficiently, resulting in high levels of sugar in the bloodstream and urine.

diaphragm: a soft rubber-like cup that covers the cervix designed to block entry of sperm into the cervix, uterus, and fallopian tubes.

diastolic pressure: the period of least pressure in the arterial vascular system, a measurement taken between beats, when the heart is at rest. With 120/80, the diastolic pressure is 80.

disability insurance: an insurance policy designed to pay a specified monthly income to the policyholder in the event that he/she becomes either temporarily or permanently incapable of working.

dysplasia: abnormal development of cells.

discount broker: a broker who charges a lower commission for buy and sell orders than a full-commission broker: typically, a discount broker does not give investment advice.

discretionary income: the amount of an individual's income available for spending after all fixed and necessary expenses (such as food, clothing and shelter) have been paid.

diversification: investing in several different companies in various industries or in several different types of investments in order to spread risk.

dividend: a corporation's pro-rata payment to its shareholders.

Dow Jones Industrial Average: an average of thirty blue chip stocks commonly used as an indicator of whether the stock market is moving "up" or "down."

E

emergency fund: an emergency fund is money set aside to allow you to weather any unexpected events or expenses in your life.

emotion: an effective rather than cognitive state of consciousness in which joy, sorrow, fear, hate, or the like is experienced; usually accompanied by certain physiological changes such as increased heartbeat, respiration, and manifested by shaking, crying, etc.

essential fatty acid: a nutrient that the body can't make but which is essential to good health.

estate planning: the process of planning for the efficient transfer of assets at one's death.

estate tax: tax imposed by a state or the federal government on the transfer of property from a deceased to his/her heirs.

executor: an individual or institution that has the task of settling the estate for the deceased.

expense: an individual's cost or obligation to meet a need or pay a debt.

F

fat: adipose tissue of the body, which serves as an energy reserve.

fertilization: the fusion of a sperm and an ovum, which produces a fertilized egg.

fetus: a developing human from 8 weeks following conception to birth.
fluid retention: failure to eliminate fluids from the body because of cardiac, renal, or metabolic disease, or a high level of salt in the body.

Form 1099: the Internal Revenue Service (IRS) form used by companies to report annual dividends and interest paid to an individual. The company paying the dividends and interest will send a copy of the form to the individual and the IRS.

free radicals: highly reactive molecular fragments, generally harmful to the body.

G

glands: organs that secrete hormones or other substances that activate or inhibit body functions or that eliminate substances from the body.

gram: unit of mass (weight); about one-twenty-eighth of an ounce.

gross income: total personal income before taxes or other deductions.

gynecology: study of diseases and disorders that affect the female reproductive system.

H

hepatitis B: highly contagious type of liver inflammation caused by a viral infection, contracted through contact with infected human blood or with people at high risk for sexually transmitted disease.

herpes: painful and contagious viral inflammatory disease of the skin that causes skin ulcers in the genital and other body areas.

high blood pressure or **hypertension**: too forceful flow of blood, which may damage the blood vessel walls, leading to heart attack, stroke or kidney failure.

high-density lipoprotein (HDL): the smallest lipoprotein that removes cholesterol from LDL cells and transports it back to the liver, where cholesterol is broken down into bile acids and excreted into the intestine.

HIV: human immunodeficiency virus, regarded as responsible for the development of AIDS.

hymen: thin, membrane-like fold of skin that partially covers the entrance to the vagina.

hyperlipidemia: high cholesterol levels.

hypertension: see **high blood pressure**.

hysterectomy: surgical removal of the uterus.

I

immune: having a high degree of resistance to a disease.

immunization: process of activating the body's immune response against a specific disease.

infection: invasion of the body by disease-causing microorganisms, such as viruses and bacteria.

inflammation: reddening and swelling of body tissue as a reaction to infection or cellular injury.

irradiation: the use of large amounts of x-rays to destroy microorganisms or tissues.

insurance (health): insurance that covers medical expenses or health care services.

insurance (homeowners): insurance that combines liability insurance and hazard insurance and protects homeowners against property and casualty damage.

insurance (life): an insurance policy that pays a death benefit to the beneficiaries when the insured dies.

K

kidney: one of a pair of organs located on each side of the lower back that filter waste products from the blood and discard them in urine.

L

laparoscope: instrument used to see into the abdominal cavity.

lesion: an injury, wound, or a simple infected patch in a skin disease.

lipoproteins: compound of a simple protein and a fat component that carry fats in the blood.

liquidity: the ability of an asset to be converted into cash quickly and without significant loss of value.

living trust: also called inter-vivo trust; a trust established during the lifetime of the person creating the trust.

LMP: last menstrual period, date that indicates the probable beginning of a pregnancy.

low-density lipoprotein (LDL): particles that are rich in cholesterol.

lumpectomy: removal of a breast cancer without removing surrounding tissue; also see **mastectomy**.

M
malignant: cancerous.

mammogram: X-ray of the breasts.

mastectomy or **radical mastectomy**: surgical removal of a breast cancer and the surrounding tissue.

meditation: the act of engaging in contemplation and reflection.

menopause: cessation of menstruation.

metabolism: the aggregate of all chemical processes that take place in living organisms resulting in growth, generation of energy, elimination of waste, and other bodily functions as they relate to the distribution of nutrients in the blood after ingestion.

metastasis: migration of cancer cells or other unhealthy cells from their original development point through the blood vessels or lymphatic system to other parts of the body.

microgram (mcg): one-millionth of a gram.

milligram (mg): a metric unit of weight equal to one-thousandth of a gram.

mind: in a human or other conscious being, the element , part or process that reasons, thinks, perceives, feels, wills, judges, etc.; the totality of conscious and unconscious mental processes; intellect or understanding.

minerals: any of a class of inorganic substances occurring in nature that are neither animal nor vegetable. Certain elements of definite chemical composition, such as iron, phosphorus, etc. essential to the physiology of animals and plants.

money: any convenient circulating medium of exchange, including coins, paper money and demand deposits used as a measure of possession, ownership or wealth; funds, capital, riches, assets.

monosaturated fat: a fat chemically constituted to be capable of absorbing additional hydrogen.

N

nanogram: one-billionth of a gram.

nervous system: the extensive, intricate network of structures that activates, coordinates and controls all the functions of the body.

neurotransmitter: brain chemicals that are involved in carrying messages to and from the brain.

NASDAQ: the National Association of Securities Dealers Automated Quotations system is a computerized system where prices are quoted for many small over the counter (OTC) securities along with many NYSE listed securities.

net income: for an individual, it is gross income minus expenses.

net worth: total assets minus total liabilities of an individual or company.

NYSE: the New York Stock Exchange is the largest national stock exchange in the US where the securities of large American companies are bought and sold.

O

occult blood: presence of blood in so small a quantity that it cannot be seen with the unaided eye.

osteoblast: bone cells that form new bone.

osteoclast: bone cells that re-absorb old bone.

osteopenia: lower-than-normal bone mass.

osteoporosis: thinning of the bones of the body, making fractures more common. After menopause, the risk of osteoporosis usually increases markedly.

ovary: one of two oval-shaped glands located in the female pelvic region that contain eggs and produce the female sex hormones estrogen and progesterone, as well as the male hormone testosterone.

ovulation: the release of an egg from one of the ovaries.

oxidation: process of combining with oxygen.

P

Pap smear: taking of a sample of cervical and vaginal cells to detect any abnormalities.

penis: male sex organ, whose glans or head is very sensitive and provides sexual pleasure; urination also occurs through this organ.

period: see **menstrual period**.

phyto-: denotes relationship to plants.

phytohormones: plant substances that are structurally and functionally similar to human steroids; they exert a very weak effect on the body.

P.I.D.: pelvic inflammatory disease, an infection of the organs in the female pelvis.

the Pill: birth-control pill that contains the female hormone estrogen or a combination of estrogen and the female hormone progesterone.

pituitary gland: the body's master gland, located at the base of the brain, which regulates growth and other bodily changes.

placebo: an inactive substance used as if it were an effective dose of a medication.

placebo response: the therapeutic result produced by the belief in a treatment.

power of attorney: a legal document that enables an individual to designate another person, the attorney-in-fact, to act on his/her behalf, and is valid for as long as the appointed individual is not disabled or incapacitated.

prenatal: before birth.

prophylaxis: steps taken to prevent diseases or their transmission.

pubis or **pubic area**: frontal bony structure of the pelvis.

pension plan: a qualified retirement plan established by a corporation or organization to provide income for its employees when they retire.

portfolio: an individual's or institution's total investment holdings.

premium: the money the owner pays to the insurance company in order to obtain life insurance protection.

prime rate: the base interest rate that commercial banks charge on loans.

Q
qi: the vital life energy which runs through the body (also known as *chi*).

R
radiation: the use of radioactive substances in the diagnosis and treatment of disease.

rectum: lower end of the colon that ends with the anus, or exit point from the body.

recession: a period of general and sustained economic decline.

return on investments: the money you earn or lose on your investment, expressed as a percentage of your original investment.

risk: the measurable possibility of economic loss.

S
serum: the watery, non-cellular liquid of the blood.

serum cholesterol: cholesterol circulating in the blood.

sexually transmitted diseases (STDs): infection caused by germs that are spread through sexual contact.

sigmoidoscopy: examination of the intestines through a flexible instrument inserted into the rectum.

soul: the principle of life and action regarded as an entity separate from the body, which is the immortal or spiritual aspect of a person.

speculum: plastic or metal instrument used to keep the vaginal wall open for medical examination and tests.

sperm: male reproductive cell that fertilizes the female egg; released from the body in semen.

spermicide: a chemical, such as Nonoxynol-9, that kills sperm.

sterilization: blocking the vas deferens in the male and the Fallopian tubes in the female to prevent fertilization.

sterility: inability to conceive a child.

steroid: group name for compounds based on the cholesterol molecule, e.g., sex hormones and corticosteroid.

stroke: damage to the brain caused by a blood clot or narrowing of a blood vessel so that the blood supply is cut off.

systolic blood pressure: the period of greatest pressure in the arterial vascular system. With 120/80, the systolic pressure is 120.

S&P 500: the Standard & Poor's 500 is an index made up of 500 blue chip stocks. The index is commonly used to measure stock market performance.

sales commission: a fee an investor pays a broker for buying or selling securities.

surrender charge: the fee an insurance company would assess against the cash value of a life insurance policy if the owner were to surrender the policy.

survivors: someone who may face emotional and sometimes financial setbacks because of your death.

T
tetanus: infectious disease that is generally introduced through a break in the skin which causes muscular spasms and gradual rigidity of the jaw, neck and abdomen.

thyroid gland: organ at the base of the neck primarily responsible for regulating the rate of metabolism.

trans-: prefix referring to something altered from the natural state, such as trans fatty acids.

trichomonas: protozoa that can cause vaginitis.

triglycerides: a combination of glycerol with three or five fatty acids.

tumor: an abnormal mass of tissue that is not inflammatory, arises without obvious cause from cells, and possesses no physiologic function.

tax shelter: in general, any means used to provide favorable tax treatment for all or part of an individual's or corporation's income.

taxable income: the amount used in the calculation of an individual's income tax liability.

trust: a legal arrangement in which an individual, the *trustor*, gives control of property to a person or institution, the *trustee*, for the benefit of the *beneficiaries*.

U
ultrasound: diagnostic technique that uses sound waves to produces images of internal conditions, such as that of an unborn child.

urine: a fluid secreted by the kidneys, transported by the ureter, stored in the bladder and voided by the urethra.

uterus: a pear-shaped, hollow, muscular organ located in the female pelvic area, in which the baby develops during pregnancy.

V
vagina: a passageway extending from the uterus to the outside of the body, functioning as a female sexual organ and the birth canal.

vaginitis: inflammation of the vagina.

virus: a minute parasitic microorganism, much smaller than bacteria, that may replicate only within a cell of a living plant or animal host.

vitamins: complex organic substances found variously in most natural foods, sometimes synthesized in the body, and sometimes produced synthetically; essential in small amounts for the regulation of the metabolism and normal growth and functioning of the body. Deficiencies of vitamins produce specific disorders.

W
waiting period: The length of time a disability policy holder must wait after submitting a claim before disability income benefits begin.

will: a legally enforceable declaration directing the disposal of a person's property's after their death.

Y
yeast: any unicellular, usually oval fungus that reproduces by budding; *candida albicans* is a type of pathogenic yeast.

yield: the interest or dividend payable on a security, expressed as a percentage of the price of the security.

Proceeds from the sale of this book benefit the
Angels for Haiti Project,
a division of the nonprofit organization
Health Through Communications
established by Dr. Carolle Jean-Murat to enhance the health,
education and well-being of the poorest, most vulnerable members
of Haitian society.

**Following the tragedies of September 11, an American bishop
said *"While others burn and bomb, we must build up and bind."***

BE AN ANGEL AND
HELP US BUILD A FUTURE
FOR THE CHILDREN OF HAITI!

Tax deductible donations can be sent to:

**Angels for Haiti Projects, Inc.
P.O. Box 2348
La Mesa, CA 91943-2348**

(Contributions to this 501(c)(3) organization
are deductible for IRS tax purposes.)

Do you want to learn more about the *Angels for Haiti Projects*?
Please visit www.healththroughcommunications.org
You can also donate online.

*To order additional copies of this book
or any other books or tapes by Dr. Carolle Jean-Murat
please visit her website at: www.drcarolle.com*

247

About the Author

Carolle Jean-Murat M.D., F.A.C.O.G.

Dr. Carolle is a board-certified Ob-Gyn, and a Fellow of the American College of Obstetricians and Gynecologists. She is fluent in five languages. Dr. Carolle has had a private practice in San Diego, California since 1982, and is the medical director for the Wellness Center for Midlife Women at Alvarado Hospital in San Diego, CA, and an advisory board member for the GE Center for Financial Learning. For more than fifteen years Dr. Carolle has provided free medical care to under-served women through Catholic Charities and St. Vincent de Paul Village, and is part of a team of educators and health-care providers that does volunteer work bi-annually in La Vallee de Jacmel, Haiti. She is also a clinical mentor for under-served students at San Diego State University and UCSD.

Dr. Carolle is the author of the award-winning books, *Menopause Made Easy: How to Make the Right Decisions for the Rest of Your Life*, and *Staying Healthy: 10 Easy Steps for Women*, available in both English and Spanish, plus *Natural Pregnancy A-Z*. She is a contributing author of *Millennium 2000: A Positive Approach* with Louise L. Hay and Friends, and is one of the ten doctors featured in *Fabulous Female Physicians* in The Women's Hall of Fame Series by Sharon & Florence Kirsh. Dr. Carolle is also a motivational speaker who brings her message of self-empowerment to women through her inspiring lectures, TV and radio appearances, books, articles, and audiocassettes.

Contact Dr. Carolle at:
>www.drcarolle.com
>www.healththroughcommunications.org
>www.financiallearning.com

249

Notes

Notes

Notes

Notes

Notes

Notes